Farming Industrial Hemp: Not Your Daddy's Tobacco

Dr. John O'Connor, Ph.D.: Author

Shawn Valor: Author and Transcriber

Kirsten Schuder: Author and Editor

Jade Lin O'Connor: Illustrator

Farming Industrial Hemp: Not Your Daddy's Tobacco

Editor and Book Designer: Kirsten Schuder

Cover design: Dr. John W. O'Connor, Ph. D.

Cover Photography: Shawn Valor

Illustrations: Jade Lin O'Connor

Farmer on cover: Ray "Goober" Carroll

Printed and bound in the United States of America.

ISBN: 978-1-928776-02-4

Publisher: Consolidated Interests, LLC. 1319 Hardys Creek Road, Jonesville, Virginia, 24263.

The Answers You Will Find in This Book:

Everything You Need to Know About Growing Hemp the Right Way

Solutions for Your Hemp Problems

Answers to Your Hemp Questions

Grow Successful and Safe Crops

Understand the Laws and Stay Out of Jail

DEDICATION

This book is dedicated to:
Our family. Without their love and support,
this project would not have occurred.
George Thomas O'Connor, II,
who we lost too early to tobacco and lung cancer.

ABOUT THE AUTHORS

Reverend Dr. John W. O'Connor, Ph. D.

As an Industrial Hemp Psychologist, Dr. O'Connor has worked with the Virginia Universities in the pilot hemp programs since 2014. Prior to the hemp pilot programs, Dr. O'Connor consulted dozens of farms in upstate New York, helping them with soil science and agricultural management. Since the 2018 Farm Bill, he has worked with scores of farms throughout the southeast region in establishing productive industrial hemp farming systems.

As an international consultant, he is currently helping farmers in Africa grow industrial hemp in their soil.

An ardent observer of human behavior, Dr. O'Connor's insightful knowledge has added volumes of helpful knowledge to understanding the agricultural industry's ever-changing regulations, including the 2018 Farms Bill's industrial hemp inclusion as a farm commodity. As a consultant, his understanding of agricultural regulations and organic farming techniques has help hundreds of farms.

He serves as President of the American Emotional Wellness Organization and Books for Charity, Inc a 501 C 3 nonprofit charity as well as Reverend to the Chapel of Light and Spiritual Awareness church. Dr. O'Connor has over three decades of therapy experience working with individuals, groups, corporations, and small businesses. He has received recognition from Google for having set a record with over a of 30k views to his reviews. LinkedIn congratulated him for being in the top 10% most viewed profiles. He is also a Certified Master Photographer with credits in multiple newspapers and magazines through the US and Canada. What seems like a lifetime ago at the beginning of his career, he graduated from the New Hampshire Police academy with honors.

Dr. O'Connor's articles have been published in sports magazines such as Fighter, RPM, Concealed Carry Magazine, and Summit Racing, for his knowledge on developing an unbeatable mental game, endurance, human performance, and self-protection. He is an IDPA Winter Nationals event winner and a Certified NRA pistol instructor.

Shawn Valor (a. k. a. John W. O'Connor, II)

Shawn Valor is a seasoned copywriter, published content creator, and novel-writing entrepreneur with 6 novels under development. He is a Master Luthier and Craftsman at Brute Force guitars where he created over 100 hand-crafted guitars, basses, and mandolins. He is a knowledgeable workaholic with 5 years experience in the hemp growing industry as an expert advisor to help make a safe and profitable yield for his clients. He partnered with Dr. John O'Connor, Ph. D. to create a book known as *Farming Industrial Hemp: Not Your Daddy's Tobacco* to help growers avoid the common issues that plague fields from their consulting experience. They will be partnering again for a book on the ultimate guide for state laws on hemp and CBD oil to help all understand what each laws means whether grower, processor, or traveler.

Kirsten Schuder, Master of Science in Mental Health Counseling

Kirsten Schuder's moniker envelops the three loves in her life: author, editor, and literary agent. As a nonfiction author, she has written hundreds of widely-quoted articles on mental health that continue to appear in books and international academic journals. Her book on academic cheating in universities is a critical look on how cheating has become a culturally accepted, worldwide phenomenon. She lives out a fruitful budding career as a fiction author with the first book in her *Inside Dweller* series, *Genesis.* One of Kirsten's editing endeavors began with Storyteller Magazine until the short story magazine shut down, parlaying into the creator and head editor of *Everything Otherworld* short story magazine. Their first issue will be available in October, 2019. As Vice President of Apex Literary Management, a boutique literary agency, she enjoys using her powers as wish-granter to help authors with unique, fabulous stories live out their wildest fantasies and become published authors. Kirsten's expertise in writing *useful* articles and books that people can understand and use to improve their lives has served to unify the ideas in this book into America's unique story as it enters the industrial hemp industry foray.

Jade Lin O'Connor

Jade Lin O'Connor is a budding illustrator and aspiring fashion diva. In her young life, she is already owner of her own business, Fashion Forward by Jade.

CONTENTS

Introduction: From My Point of View

It has been a very educational year as a licensed grower and processor of industrial hemp in the state of Virginia. We added a consulting service to our lineup to help farmers with the transition and problems of growing hemp. We received so many phone calls from residents wanting to grow hemp and abandon tobacco because all the news agencies reported how hemp will be the new cash crop. CNN even put out a release that you *cannot smoke it!* Thus, everyone ran out and bought the highest percentage of CBD flower seeds they could their hands on to grow at exorbitant prices thinking they were going to make a killing this season. None of the farmers I spoke with have any experience growing cannabis products and are being misled by so-called tobacco industry experts on how to grow a crop none of them ever grew before, who also know nothing of the legal aspect of growing hemp. From what I have been told, these so-called experts are telling everyone to grow hemp exactly like tobacco. Good luck with that.

We have made many contacts in the industry in the past few years, including labs, growers in many states, other processors, dispensary owners, university professors, magazines, online stores and too many more to list here. As with all other brand-new industries, you have to be on the lookout for predators making huge claims and false claims to turn a buck. For example, I spoke with a local store who claimed that "nanobytes" were used to produce their CDB products. It seems the hemp industry is attracting its share of con-artists and frauds looking to make a quick buck at everyone else's expense.

You also have your share of people claiming to be consultants who have never grown the product in their life but seem to think they can tell everyone how to grow industrial hemp perfectly without issues. What makes this worse is that the USDA has taken a step back and refused to institute regulations for hemp farmers until 2020, stating they are waiting on hemp to implode on itself this growing season. Now we are all waiting on the FDA to hand down its regulations on CBD products; their legality hangs in the balance. Their decision will be a game-changer and could ruin the whole hemp industry. As Chapter 14 will cover, state agencies are already doing a fine job of this themselves. If the country continues to go in this direction, the only people who will benefit from hemp are the people who already have a strong foothold in the industry through legalized marijuana.

Every person interested in jumping into the industry must do so with head, not feet, first. This book was written to protect you and your interests from bad advice and consumer fraud that could lead to jail time. I hope you will find this book educational as well as indispensable.

Happy growing!

Dr. John W. O'Connor, Ph. D.: Industrial Hemp Psychologist

Part I

The Hemp Industry: A Brief Introduction

A tobacco field

1. INDUSTRIAL HEMP'S POTENTIAL AND ITS POTENTIAL CONSEQUENCES

Hemp is already a booming business and a future superpower industry in the United States. Yearly revenue for hemp has reached 20 billion U. S. dollars, and projected earnings are estimated to hit 500 billion by 2030. In contrast, the tobacco industry is on the decline in the United States due to low-priced foreign competitors. Many tobacco companies including Marlboro have already invested billions of dollars in the cannabis industry. Success stories abound in states such as California, Colorado, and Oregon. In other areas around the U.S. that recently legalized the substance in step with the 2018 Farm Bill, industrial hemp is still in its infancy, but over time and under the right conditions to foster industry growth, industrial hemp will blossom in all states and follow projected growth as in the pioneer states.

Many from the southern region are looking to replace their tobacco crops with industrial hemp. While hemp, for certain, is not a traditional crop to grow in the United States, its multiple industrial uses make it a super crop in comparison to other agricultural products. Its uses do not end at "smokables" and consumables. The plant's use in medicinal items such as CBD oil, biofuel, car manufacturing, paper, cooking flour, bottles, clothing, and even beauty products are all undeveloped applications of the industrial hemp plant. Hemp has the potential to be used in every facet in our daily lives when the industry blossoms to its full potential.

On the other hand, the tobacco industry is on the decline due to regulations, monopolies, and foreign competition, making it a challenge for U. S. farmers to earn a living, in addition to the health consequences of tobacco consumption. According to Forbes Globenewswire.com, even a mediocre industrial hemp crop can bring in more profit then tobacco. Ideally, though, farmers strive to raise healthy crops with a full realization of its potential. Hemp done right can yield high profit, lower lawsuit risk, and safeguard your grower license, which are all the objectives of this book series.

Much like the bitcoin boom and any other investment, hemp carries with it some risk. Farmers need to educate themselves in the required licenses, the rules for growing, legal growing limits, and your state's interpretation of the Farm Bill for the legality of the growing, sale, and distribution of hemp. Without the right licenses, you may not even be able to touch your hemp plants after growing them.

In addition to licensing requirements, the legality of industrial hemp makes it a risky crop to grow in states where marijuana is not legal, especially in these beginning phases of the industry; the manner in which farmers grow the plant becomes the primary concern. The way you grow your hemp could be the difference between profits and jail time. Tobacco farmers turned "hemp experts" will try and convince you to grow your hemp crops like tobacco. The Feds recommend to plant hemp seeds like corn. While they are all agricultural commodities, tobacco, corn, and hemp are different plants.

If you want to stake your claim in industrial hemp, it takes more effort than throwing it in the ground and watching it grow. Buying clones and seeds to grow hemp, especially on large scale is very costly and not guaranteed to return your investment. Without a good crop, your chances dip significantly. Following the wrong advice in growing a good plant could leave you with sickly plants or "hot" crops that the DEA might force you to burn because the plants went over the legal THC limits, causing a loss of thousands of dollars and all of the time and effort it took you to plant and harvest instead of enjoying the fruits of your crop and the profits it can yield. A bad crop will leave plants that are unsellable, and instead of making the $3000 per plant canna speakers claim if you can sell the plant by the gram, you'll make $30 per plant if you're lucky, or worse, the DEA will force you to burn your whole crop and your entire investment with it. Even a hundredth of a percent over your state's legal THC limits can lead to your crop getting reported and burned. Many states have very strict regulations on growing and processing. Breaking those regulations can have severe consequences, including revoking your license and punishment as severe as time in prison. If the crop goes over 0.30, which is known as "delta-9" in the Farm Bill, your agricultural department or the police, who will test your plants depending on your state, will report your crop to the DEA, who in turn will require you to burn your crop. If local law enforcement finds you negligent in your growing practices, they can throw you into jail for up to three years for growing marijuana. This is what happens to growers who do not take the time to learn how to grow hemp within legal THC limits.

Proper care and growing practices produce healthy, tall plants that fall within legal THC limits. It also takes the ability to know what you're looking to grow and how to make sure it grows so that you will get consistent and desired results. You have to know how to control the plants throughout each part of the growing cycle. Without that knowledge, it can lead to severe consequences for you.

In addition to protecting your interests, if you grow hemp for human and animal consumption, good growing practices and precautions can protect you from future lawsuits. In this industry, because of the many regulations, you have to know those rules and what steps you have to take to verify you're crop is legal and safe.

Finally, you have to know what product you're going to sell and how to grow that strain right. For example, if you want to get into the "smokables," if your CBD percentage comes in too low because you bought the wrong variety or if it goes to seed, not even dog food manufacturers will buy your plants. Without the correct licenses, you will not be able to even remove the seeds in your own plants if your crop goes to seed.

By the end of this book, you'll be fluent in growing industrial hemp. You'll learn:

- The differences in soil needs of the plants, the different growing care needed
- The different hemp strains that are out there
- What strain you will need for the product you want to grow and sell
- How to create the ideal growing platform for hemp
- How to turn your previous tobacco field into a hemp field
- How to take care of the plant at each stage
- How to identify male and female plants
- The growing practices to avoid
- The state of the current hemp marketplace
- How to dry your hemp plant properly and what happens if you don't
- How to maximize the sell-ability of your crop
- How to ensure you're safe in growing within legal THC limits
- How current state guidelines and testing practices can produce a strike against your license even when you have grown a legal product

This book series will become part of your arsenal to ensure that you can grow hemp legally, safely, and profitably. The more people who follow legitimate practices, the more the hemp industry will grow, flourish, and provide a viable income and way of life for all involved.

In this chapter, we reviewed some reasons to invest in and become involved with the industrial hemp industry. We listed the many reasons for hemp's viability as a profitable commodity. We also explained the reasons why all who want to become involved with hemp should proceed with caution, eyes, ears, and minds wide open: there are certain federal and state legislation that all growers are expected to follow. Regardless of the reason the plants go over the legal THC levels, failure to comply with federal and state laws could result in jail time, depending on the situation and the level of neglect, left to the discretion of local authorities who are most likely not pro-pot.

In order to become knowledgeable hemp industry professionals, growers should become familiar with standard industry terms. Chapter 2 will define some of the most common industry terms so you can easily converse with other industry professionals using the terminology appropriately and knowledgeably.

2. DEFINITION OF INDUSTRIAL HEMP AND OTHER TERMINOLOGY

As with all industries, the hemp industry has its share of jargon. Because it is a newer industry, there can be some confusion in the definition of the terms used. Moreover, the creation of new definitions crop up frequently, adding to the fracas. For these reasons, many people have developed an inaccurate understanding of the main industry terms. This chapter will clear the air and establish a basic understanding of industrial hemp and its varieties as well as why it is distinguished from marijuana. The end of the chapter will offer an accurate list of terms.

What Is Industrial Hemp?

Industrial hemp is the cousin of marijuana. Its scientific name is Cannabaceae Sativa, under the cannabis family. Hemp is a fast-growing crop, the fastest-growing cannabis plant. It can grow up to 20 feet in an extended growing season.

What sets the marijuana and cannabis apart is THC level, the psychoactive substance in marijuana that produces the "high" feeling. Hemp is legally defined as any cannabis species being under 0.30% THC. Any hemp or marijuana variety exceeding 0.30% THC is legally considered marijuana regardless of strain, variety, and type. For instance, when high-CBD hemp is mixed with high-THC marijuana to create hybrid plants, those plants are considered marijuana with high CBD amount.

CBD oil is considered a hemp product and it is what defines hemp in its species. Marijuana varieties have high THC and lower CBD content. CBD contains many medicinal properties. Hemp is less psychoactive than marijuana due to the low THC content.

Thus, the term industrial hemp refers to the industrial use of CBD, fiber, and seeds. Hemp has multi-industrial use, and strains have been developed to cultivate the part of the plant to emphasize the characteristics of the plant. For instance, if one were to cultivate hemp for its wood and fiber, certain strains will develop plants with thick stalks. Hemp was defined to have use in over 25,000 industries.

Industrial Hemp: A Brief History and Why It Was Illegalized

Hemp has been used since the dawn of man about 10,000 years ago for fabric, and then later for sails and concrete. Many stone buildings were made with hemp concrete during the middle ages. Hemp has been used in industry up until the 1940s for materials during World War II. "Call to Hemp" was proclaimed as farmers grew millions of tons of hemp to be used in the war. Hemp was used as rope on all ships during the colonial era, and many colonies in America required all its citizens to grow hemp.

However, the tide of public opinion changes in the early 1940s. Hemp was reclassified with illegal drugs as part of a political campaign with Andrew Mellon at the helm, who was head of the Bank of Pittsburgh and Treasury Secretary. DuPont became involved and backed Mellon for their own interests: they desired to promote and manufacture their newly-developed nylon to use in their paints. Even though nylon was eventually found to be severely toxic and outlawed in the '50s-'60s, hemp was never reinstituted for industrial purposes until this decade.

What Is Marijuana?

Also known as Cannabis Indica, it is a plant species known for high THC. It is used for medical and recreation consumption. The THC amounts can go from over 0.30% to 30% in the plant. The THC amount creates euphoria and is used for many physical conditions and pain relief. Marijuana has been used as a natural medicine for ailments for over 3000 years.

Industrial Hemp vs. Pot

There are basic differences between hemp and marijuana that distinguish the two cousin plants from each other:

- Hemp grows thinner and taller than marijuana. Marijuana grows wide and bushy, while hemp grows upward and tall.
- Hemp has thin, spread-out leaves while marijuana has wide, close-together leaves.
- Hemp has minimal THC amounts while having high CBD amounts reaching up to 30%.
- Marijuana has low CBD levels and high THC amounts up to 30%.
- Hemp is more profitable for industry use because of its fast and quick growth.
- Hemp's low THC amount, when it does not go "hot," makes it a safe plant to grow and has multiple industry applications.
- When consumed, hemp's CBD creates a more energetic feeling and reduces stress.
- Marijuana's THC has a sedative effect.

Why Hemp Is Legal

In the 2014 Farm Bill, the U. S. federal government allowed states to establish programs to grow industrial hemp on a trial research basis. For four years, universities around the country researched hemp agriculture. A lot of the research we read from this period had to do with growing conditions within the states and whether or not the plants maintained legal THC levels. The 2018 Farm Bill declassified hemp as a Class III controlled substance, placing it on par with regular agricultural products such as corn and potatoes.

Because industrial hemp has been declassified, hemp is finding its way to the mainstream its many industrial uses, mainly with fibers for construction and seed for food. It can be grown like corn and grows very tall, which provides a lot of usable material for-profit and product making. CBD has been gaining recognition as an effective anti-anxiety medication in comparison to products that contain high THC, but without the hallucinogenic effects of THC, allowing people to participate fully in their jobs. In addition, CBD does not contain any of the side effects THC has been known to contain, including anxiety and paranoia.

What is CBD?

CBD is the main psychoactive chemical in hemp called a Cannabinoid. CBD is a nonintoxicating relaxant that can be uplifting, and it can relieve pain symptoms without the "high" effect of marijuana. It is extracted from the stalk, leaves, and buds of the female hemp plant, with the bud/flower containing the highest amount of CBD. The seeds do not contain any CBD in them and can only produce hemp oil, which is more like cooking oil. The higher the CBD amount, the longer and stronger the effects last. Higher quality plants with high CBD, over 10%, are desired for consumable and CBD oil products.

What Is Grain Hemp?

Grain is the meal and edible product made from seed. Seeds are high in fatty oils and iron making it a very healthy meal. In terms of seed output, the strain is usually referred to as "grain." This is where pollination of the females by the male plants is desired. The females will produce many pounds of seed instead of flower. That seed can be made into flour, hemp oil, or other grain. The flour is a great gluten-free substitute for standard white flour.

What Is Fiber?

Hemp is most widely used for its fiber. Hemp fiber variations are characterized by its long stems, little and few branches, and low flower. There are many markets for hemp fiber. Hemp fiber is useful because of hemp's long length of up to 20 feet, quick growth, which creates useful long strands for processing into products. The hemp stalk contains stringy strands that are less flexible than flax, another plant harvested for fiber. Hemp can produce 2-3X more fiber annually than cotton. Hemp fabric is one of the oldest industries with the first dating back to 8000 B.C. Hemp is one of the most durable and strongest of all textile fibers and products made from hemp will outlast all others by many years. It's easy to see that hemp is a very high-quality product. Hemp clothing does not fade, and because of its porous nature, it does not shrink in hot water temperatures. Hemp could overtake cotton, polyester, and linen in the future.

What Is Flower?

The buds in hemp are referred to as "flower." However, they are similar in appearance to the buds in marijuana. Hemp flowers have high CBD and low THC. They can be consumed through smoking and eating to have an anti-anxiety effect, but many flowering strains can also have an energizing effect, similar to a caffeine rush. The buds have trichomes, which are like little transparent sticky fingers that contain the resin which contains all the CBD and THC. The burning of the bud releases the CBD, although not as efficiently as through the extraction process, and converts the THC-A to THC, which makes the THC-A into a psychoactive substance. Many different varieties of strains of been developed to maximize the CBD contained in hemp flowers. Some examples of these types of strains are Special Sauce, Buddha's Delight, Cherry wine, AC/DC, and Berry Blossom. New strains are often developed to drive the CBD levels higher. One aspect of this strain of hemp that growers should be aware of is that the THC percentage can vary from bud to bud. For this reason, it can be the riskiest hemp product to grow at this point of time in U. S. history.

What Is THC?

THC is the general overarching term of the psychoactive chemicals present in marijuana and the cannabis family. Delta-9 THC, the level of measurement procured from a fully burned sample of a hemp bud, is the main ingredient in the feeling of getting "high." THC has the power to over-stimulate the receptors at high amounts and cause a reaction of paranoia or anxiety. CBD can counter those effects THC can cause, which allows for full relaxation. Both chemicals THC and CBD have medicinal properties.

High THC is mostly found in marijuana and hybrid hemp, while present even in small amounts in all cannabis species. THC in amounts over 0.3% are considered illegal in many states that don't allow marijuana and can get you convicted of a Class I Felony.

What Are Hybrids?

Hybrids are combinations of Indica (marijuana) and Sativa (hemp). All those varieties are illegal in hemp states due to their high THC content, which qualifies it as marijuana regardless of the hemp strain. Hybrid hemp *should not* be sold to hemp-legal states without legal recreational marijuana laws. Hybrid hemp has the benefits of high CBD and high THC and can be used for recreational consumption, making high CBD oil, and making high THC and CBD oil. They can provide the benefits of THC without the worry of paranoia. Some high THC hemp can have high CBD like hemp, up to 16%, and can produce a relaxing effect like marijuana. Many hybrids come more from marijuana with hemp traits, while hot hemp qualifies as hemp with marijuana traits.

List of Common Terms

Now that we have established some important distinctions between industrial hemp and marijuana, we have provided a quick-and-easy list of terms for you so you can become well-versed in "hempese," the language of the hemp industry.

Bud: A common name of the flower that cannabis grows, which is crumbled and either smoked or eaten for medicinal and recreational use.

CBD: A naturally-occurring chemical extracted from the buds, flowers, and leaves of the hemp plant. CBD is thought to have calming, anti-anxiety, and pain-relieving effects and is often found in consumable products.

CBD Oil: The refined oil extract of hemp used for consumption, vaping, or smoking. It offers the consumer a chance to feel the benefits of CBD without smoking the buds or tasting hemp.

Clone: A cutting from a grown female plant (mother) that, when planted into the soil, will produce a full-grown plant identical to the mother plant.

Delta-9 THC: The converted tetrahydrocannibol acid obtained when THC-A is separated from the hemp plant and then super-heated to produce a neutral substance. Also the line of demarcation according to the 2018 Farm Bill between hemp (below 0.30% THC) and marijuana (0.30% THC and above).

Fiber: The strands in the stalk of hemp.

Flower: Commonly known as bud, it is found in all cannabis species. Flower is where you find the trichomes that contain the THC and CBD.

High CBD: Includes CBD levels over 10% and going all the way up to 30%.

High THC: A plant that came back from tests over the legal limit of delta-9 by a large margin, anywhere between 5% and 30%.

Hot: A hemp plant that went over legal limits of 0.30% delta-9 THC. Severe consequences exist for farmers who grow plants that go over the limit on hemp. Anything higher than 0.30%, and the authorities treat the hemp plant the same as its illegal cousin, pot.

Hybrid: A mix of hemp and marijuana to produce a plant that is high in the chemicals CBD and THC.

Industrial Hemp: A plant of the cannabis family known as Cannabaceae Sativa containing low THC and low to high CBD percentage. The plant has applications across multiple industries, and the entire plant, seeds, stalks, and roots, all have a wide variety of applications.

Marijuana: A plant of the cannabis family known as Cannabaceae Indica, high in the chemical THC and low in the chemical CBD

Smokables: A possible product of the hemp plant after processing. The buds/flowers are packaged and sold for consumers to smoke in a pipe or a "joint" (hemp cigarette).

THC-A: The non psychoactive precursor to <u>Delta-9 THC</u> in its natural form, as an acid before it converts to its psychoactive form, THC. When heated it turns into delta-9 THC.

THC: A general term referring to delta-9 THC, a psychoactive substance that creates the "high" feeling. Derived from THC-A when the plant is burned or heated.

<u>Total THC</u>: A value often used in place of the delta-9 value according to the 2018 Farm Bill, calculated using the formula of (THC) x .877 + (THC-A). Some states use TOTAL THC as the standard of legal levels of THC in hemp plants rather than delta-9 THC as outlined in the Farm Bill. This measurement takes into account the THC in acid form.

Trichomes: Miniscule "fingers" on the buds and leaves of hemp containing the CBD and THC in the plant. Trichomes are also present on the leaves of tobacco, which creates the stickiness of the leaf.

In this chapter, we covered some of the most common terms used throughout the hemp industry. They are also terms that cause the most confusion among new growers and processors. Necessarily, legality is integrated into many of the terms.

While hemp is often compared to other agricultural commodities, most often tobacco, Chapter 3 will provide an explanation of why treating hemp like other plants is a big mistake that can waste all of your time, money, and resources, and can even get you in trouble with the law.

3. "EGGPLANTS VS. ROSES": WHY GROWERS SHOULD NOT TREAT HEMP LIKE TOBACCO

"Roses vs. eggplants" is meant as a comparison for hemp vs. tobacco growing. If you've ever grown roses, you know how finicky the plant can be. Eggplants are less finicky and hardier. In addition, they are completely different plants. They have different soil and care requirements.

We can apply the same comparison to hemp and tobacco. The only aspects hemp and tobacco have in common is the presence of trichomes on the leaves and buds, both plants go through a drying process after harvesting, and both plants soak up what's in the soil like sponges. We are looking at two completely different plants, and tobacco is the hardier and less work-intensive of the two plants. Trying to grow the two the same way is like trying to use tractor parts on a Ferrari. It doesn't work. If you don't know the differences between these two plants, you are setting yourself up for failure.

One piece of advice we have heard from tobacco farmers who refer to themselves as the experts in hemp is that tobacco farmers who want to convert their fields to hemp fields can plant the hemp right into the tobacco plots and then carry on as before, with all of the same farming practices as they applied to tobacco. This is the worst advice we've heard to date. Tobacco is demanding on the soil and saps nutrients from the field that hemp needs to grow and thrive. Standard fertilizers will not replace what tobacco had taken from the sandy clay soil found in the southern region. Also, hemp does not grow well in the same conditions as tobacco.

By the time you've grown the hemp crop in tobacco conditions in an old tobacco plot, you will end up with small, fungus-ridden, bug-ridden, 2 to 4-foot plants that begin to die while still in the ground. This is not a hypothetical situation. This is what we've seen with our own eyes. Farmers have a very difficult time selling these plants even as biomass, the lowest-paying market. When farmers know how to maximize the ideal conditions, hemp plants can grow to approximately 7 feet in height. When you grow hemp plants in tobacco conditions, you are depriving your plants of the chemicals they need to thrive that are specific to this species.

Even the drying process of the two plants differs vastly, and at this pivotal period for hemp, it can mean the difference between having something you can sell or something you have to burn in a pile. If left in standard conditions to dry or left in an aired barn to dry like tobacco, the plant is at risk to go to bugs, fungus, and rot, which the plant is very susceptible to compared to tobacco. As the grower, it is your responsibility to dry the hemp plants and make sure they are in safe sellable condition.

While tobacco thrives under the hot, humid conditions of the southern summers and the sandy clay soil of the south, hemp's ideal growing conditions differ. The ideal growing conditions of hemp are semi-humid air, dark nutrient-filled topsoil—at least 4-6 feet—a relative temperature of under 85 degrees, and relatively low rainfall. Too much humidity, between 85% and 100%, and the plant is at risk for developing fungi and mold in the plants and stalks and stunt its growth. Too much rain will drown the plants and increase the risk of bug penetration via plant mold. Extreme heat above 85 degrees for several days will dry it up beyond the repair. Sandy soil will lead to nutrient-deficient stunted plants, and since sandy clay soil saturates easily, too much rain can drown hemp plants. For hemp, it's imperative to control the environment of the plant during all conditions to ensure the plant will grow. Growing outside still needs a controlled environment or else the crop could die. Unfortunately, most of these worst-case scenario conditions are a constant reality for the southern region in the growing season, making hemp a less-than-ideal plant to grow large scale in the southern region. Tobacco under these very same conditions can grow and thrive.

Tobacco is also well-suited to grow in the mountainous regions of the south, namely the Appalachian Mountains. Tobacco can grow on hilly terrain while hemp would be harmed in such conditions due to soil runoff. Hemp's high need for nutrients means that the hill runoff will stunt the plant. Soil runoff from high-grade hills could pull the plant out of the ground during its youth, meaning you lose your plant before it even develops.

Tobacco can grow well in sandy clay-based soil and has for hundreds of years. Sandy clay soil also tends to be either high in acidity or alkalinity, which will burn the roots of the hemp plant. Tobacco will thrive in a pH of 5.7-6.2 while hemp will burn and die in soil pH of 7.0 or higher or soils under 6.0. Nutrients also have a more difficult time traveling through hard clay soil. The southern U. S. region has a prevalence of clay soil, while the western and Midwestern regions contain dark loam soil that's more ideal for hemp growth, hence the success of those states in the hemp industry. Clay soil tends to become sticky when wet and hard to cultivate.

Despite the fact that the tobacco growers turned "hemp experts" recommend to tobacco farmers to dry hemp just like tobacco, the harvesting and drying practices of hemp are unavoidably different from tobacco. Hemp must be dried in a controlled environment. Cutting hemp at the stalk and leaving it in the field, as is common with tobacco harvesting, will expose it to bugs on the ground surface and mildew, which will cause it to mold.

Tobacco drying in field

Hemp drying on racks

Once the plant molds, it is difficult to sell any part as a smokable or anything else. People smoking the bud would be smoking the mold and fungi, which no store or processor wants when there are many more growers out there around the nation who grow hemp without mold, bugs, and fungi on the plant. Fungi and mold are a huge problem in hemp, and if it's not dried properly, it will grow mold and fungi which will lead you to a loss of potential income and your initial financial investment. Even worse, if your plant goes to fungi, mold, and bugs, you may not be able to fix the plants to be ready to sell, such as removing fungus-ridden leaves or breaking apart the buds to separate the bugs from the buds. In many states, you can't manipulate the plant's flower or buds without a processors license, so even if you have problems with your plants, you will not be able to shed its leaves or pick apart your buds to take out bugs or seeds. Doing so will cause you to lose your license.

Taking care to follow planting and growing practices from the start helps farmers produce viable and safe products. Growing industrial hemp is a very scientific process because of its needs to be in perfect condition to sell it for consuming for the mass market. For example, it's important to start your hemp plant in sterilized 2-gallon containers before putting them in the ground. It takes about 3 weeks for hemp to develop enough to plant outside. The product you put out for people to consume has to be a viable and safe product for people and/animals to consume. An improperly grown plant will affect your final product, which will leave you out in the cold when it is time to sell your plants.

Hemp plants have a shelf life. They remain fresh for several months, but then, as time passes, they become less attractive to buyers. They will not buy a product that is over a year old when the promise of obtaining fresh hemp exists every single growing season. A hemp plant will not keep for years on end, especially when already invaded by mold and fungi. You will have to burn your plant, especially if you want to grow the next season. The only way to really eradicate your fungus-ridden plants from infecting your next year's crop is to burn it as far away as possible from your growing field; otherwise, the fungi can spread to your new plants.

The FDA has not regulated hemp products or the CBD produced from it at this point and time, but the press still reports on CBD products that contain contaminants. There is still a need for an ethical guideline for growing to produce a safe legal consumable product for the mass market. Without ethical guidelines, many of the products put out for consumers to take in will be sub-par, poisoned, and lack of confidence in the whole hemp industry leading to a loss of profit for all. All it would take is one person's death for the government to shut down the whole industry in a heartbeat. As of 2020, the USDA is waiting on putting through regulations; instead, they expect the whole hemp industry to implode in on itself through overproduction and plants going hot.

In short, tobacco will grow in bad soil, but it takes a lot of toxic and poisonous pesticides and fungicides to make it grow. Because of tobacco's high correlation with cancer, not much care is employed to grow tobacco in nontoxic conditions. In comparison, hemp will not thrive in those conditions and will be under severe scrutiny by federal officials, because of the negative association it has with marijuana despite the fact that <u>overdose</u> is highly unlikely. A person would have to smoke a 47-pound joint in one sitting.

However, many states are stepping in and ensuring the safety of hemp from the start, which prohibits some common tobacco farming practices in hemp growing. If you listen to tobacco-growers-turned-hemp-experts, they will recommend you use the same pesticides on your hemp plants as with tobacco. In some states such as <u>Virginia,</u> there are firm regulations on hemp as there are in <u>many other states</u>. The state prohibits the use of pesticides and insecticides, and they will test your product in a lab to ensure compliance. If you listened to some tobacco growers trying to tell you how to grow hemp, you will find they will recommend including the pesticides. In doing so, you will end up with stunted mediocre plants. In addition, you will gain a bad reputation: no buyers in other states, such as Colorado, want your product either, demanding a pesticide and insecticide-free product.

Tobacco is generally known as a toxic product that produces a host of <u>health problems</u>, such as emphysema, heart disease, and lung, throat, and tongue cancer. Much of this can have to do with their growing practices, and it behooves hemp growers to avoid such growing practices to avoid producing toxic products. In tobacco, many companies produce cigarettes that contain enough alpha waves where smoking a package and half of cigarettes every day would be equivalent to <u>300 x-rays</u> per year.

Can you imagine the same level of toxicity in hemp products with the entire consumable market? Consumers see hemp as a health product. Hemp can be made into flour and chocolate. Its seeds can be ground up and made into a protein powder. Hemp oil is sold on supermarket shelves. If you include tobacco practices in the product you grown, you could be feeding your family a radioactive cake or smoothie, especially if you grow it in the same ground as tobacco fields. This is scary, because these facts can ensure that this radiation winds up in your hemp plants, and this is what you risk growing hemp like tobacco. In a later chapter, we will explain the process of this outcome.

We can't expect two different plants to do the same thing as we cannot expect from two separate people. Two people will act differently and have different needs and desires. They will approach a task in two different ways. Those two people will have two different relationships with you, they will treat you differently, and that's something you can't change about them. You can't make one act like the other. Therefore you will have to treat those two people differently. You can't treat those two people the same or else you might hurt your relationship with them. You will have to take hemp and tobacco for what they are: two separate entities that have to be treated and raised two different ways if you want success.

As this chapter explained, tobacco and hemp plants have some similarities. However, treating hemp just like tobacco will cause you to produce a toxic, stunted product. Any instructions "experts" provide in growing, harvesting, and drying hemp "just like tobacco" is unscientific and should be thrown out as pop culture bandwagon propaganda.

Returning to our analogy, eggplants versus roses, we challenge you to grow your roses like eggplants and see how your roses fair. Roses versus eggplants came from a conversation with a grower in Virginia. This person did not understand what the difference was in growing hemp and tobacco and did not know why they kept getting a bad crop. The person finally understood when I used the comparison of "roses versus eggplants." The hardiness of an eggplant versus the difficulty of growing a rose, a rose requires special treatment while an eggplant is a hardy plant that can grow in most environments and doesn't require that much hands-on care to succeed. Hemp is the rose in this comparison, and tobacco is the eggplant. Hemp is a very delicate plant that takes science and constant care and checkup. It fails when grown in tobacco conditions, even with care.

In Part II, we will describe the different pieces of information you will need to choose the best growing site for your hemp crop. Selecting and developing the best growing site for your plants will help create the ultimate growing environment for your hemp crop and protect your investment.

Hemp on one side, tobacco on the other

Part II

Planning I: Site Selection and Preparation

Greenhouse

4. GROWING IN GREENHOUSES, HOTHOUSES, HOOPHOUSES AND OTHER ALTERNATIVE STRUCTURES FOR THE ULTIMATE HEMP-GROWING ENVIRONMENT

As the last chapter established, there are many variables in hemp growing that make the plant unique. In a greenhouse, you can easily control your atmosphere and limit complications. There are a number of advantages to growing in greenhouses and other types of structures. The following is a quick list of how your life will become easier if you decide to grow your plants in a greenhouse.

- If your soil or any of your fields are not suitable for hemp, in a greenhouse, this is not an issue. In a greenhouse, you can use fertilizer in containers to grow hemp, which allows you the flexibility to use the right nutrients in your fertilizer and the right compost.

- Greenhouses can help you keep out pests and animals. If you have a concrete floor or have a general floor that the greenhouse will help keep out ground pests such as moles, mice, groundhogs, and rabbits from getting to your plants and affecting them. The plastic can be a deterrent from deer or escaped farm animals from getting to your crop and contaminating it as well. We do suggest that you fence in your greenhouses in case a farm animal does escape, pigs and goats might try to break through the plastic and leave a hole.

- Greenhouses keep the rain out so you can control the watering you can give your hemp plants so they won't mold or wilt from overwatering. This can take extra work if you plan on doing it by hand. However, you can buy a watering system that mounts to the top of greenhouses to help with automation.

- You won't have to worry about your plants burning because of a greenhouse's customizability. You can change the air temperature through fans and air conditioning in a greenhouse, while the plastic cover will let light in without the brunt of the sun's heat. If need be, if your greenhouse gets too hot from the sun's heat, you can cover with black plastic during the hot weather and use UV lights to make up for the lost light.

- With a greenhouse, you can grow year-round. You have full control of the environment. Winter is no longer an issue; in a greenhouse, you can simulate the perfect growing range for hemp with lights and heat lamps. It doesn't matter if you're growing in the ground, raised beds, or containers: a greenhouse's design creates the perfect recipes for growing any kind of plant. Cannabis itself thrives in a greenhouse setting.

For all of the above reasons, since flowers are considered a consumable item, if you are thinking of growing flower to sell to CBD processers, you might want to heavily consider putting up greenhouses and growing your plants in there. A greenhouse is essential for growing flower varieties. Flower varieties are far more temperamental in the environment they are grown in, so it is important to be able to control that so you can sell your whole crop. For a good crop, you can yield $20 per 1 gram bud from a standard, well-developed 6-to-8-foot, one-pound hemp plant. For plants in poor condition, you might only get a couple of cents per bud. The market for growing and selling flower varieties is very competitive, and producing the highest quality can make you a lot of money. Many states have growers who have already been growing hemp and its cousin, marijuana, for a good number of years. They have a good head start and well-established channels for which to sell their product. In addition, their hemp flowers and plants are in great condition because they grew them in greenhouses.

Greenhouses give you the advantage if things go wrong, and they can go wrong quickly. All it takes is one good rainstorm with several hours of 100% humidity, and that's all it takes to develop mold and fungus. You have to be able to adjust the environment in a heartbeat, which is a lot to do in a greenhouse setting and nearly impossible in a field setting. The greenhouse gives the flower strains the best opportunity to fully develop its DNA and roots to produce the maximum amount of CBD. It's going to maximize the genetic potential and can help you be able to produce 2-3 pounds of bud per plant. It helps control so that your plants do not pick up any fungal diseases or bug-related issues. If a fungal disease does take over your plant, it will eliminate the CBD content and even if it goes to harvest. The end product will be low CBD and nearly worthless because it will not be safe for smoking or consumption in oil. Greenhouses give you the best opportunity to react quickly and respond and alter the environment for your plants.

It is also easier checking for male hemp plants in a greenhouse environment than in a field as you can keep track of each plant per bucket. (Identifying males will be discussed in the growing section.) You can activate flower mode early in a greenhouse by giving it a specific amount of light time and dark time, which will tell you if a seedling is male or female early, so you don't have to find out when the hemp plant is fully grown. You can then switch hemp back around to vegetative mode for it to continue growing to its full potential once you remove the males in your crop. In a field environment, it can be difficult and laborious to find a male plant in a crop of a thousand plants that you would only know around flowering time when it's too late. In a field, hemp benefits when you crowd them together during planting so the plant can crowd out competing weeds. Buds that go to seed from male plants germinating the females sell for a lot less even if they are good quality.

A clean greenhouse that has all of the bells and whistles can give you full control of your environment. However, one that does not have the needed utilities won't benefit you as much. A greenhouse can get very humid without the right airflow, indoor fans, exhaust fans, and even dehumidifier. Humidity can become a breeding ground for fungi and bug attacks, but the benefit is you may rarely see it so long as you keep your clothing, working utensils, and shoes clean. A greenhouse can be allowed to be a clean environment to ensure consumer safe plants and it takes that extra professional step to make the highest quality hemp plants. Washing down tools and using clean clothing will ensure and E.coli and microbial free hemp crop and should be the national standard for consumable hemp.

In greenhouses, you will be limited to how much you can grow—the advantage of growing hemp outdoors on your farmland. A 30-gallon container per hemp plant will allow the plant's roots to fully develop. Anything smaller will stunt the root system and growth. This will limit you on space needed per plant, so the bigger the greenhouse the more you can grow, the closer it is to the amount you can grow in a field. Nevertheless, the complication that can come from growing in a field, whether you are growing clones, seeds, or flower for buds or CBD, the best way to grow it is in a greenhouse. Thus, greenhouses are the preferred way to grow for flower varieties, the largest developed market in the United States at this time. However, there are other options to greenhouses that parallel greenhouses.

Even if you don't have the property to put up a greenhouse, it doesn't mean you can't put up or acquire a growhouse. Many people in Tennessee are using growhouses, a huge trend in this state. It's another option from outdoor growing. You don't need a farm or open land to grow. The next best thing to a greenhouse is a growhouse, one that you set up with the right lights, humidity control, and exhaust fans. Many people are growing 1000 plants or more in growhouses. The plants can equal the quality in of greenhouse-grown hemp because you have full control over the environment. Any prefab, steel span, old garage, or old house can be converted to a growhouse. In a growhouse, though, you will most likely have to supply all of the light. There is the added expense of buying full-spectrum grow lights and supplying all of the electricity to run the lights for at least twelve hours a day for a few months at a time.

In a hoophouse, you can plant in the ground rather than pots, saving on the costs for acquiring hundreds or thousands of grow buckets. The benefits of a hoophouse are easy construction, low cost, and a strong, metal frame. They are so common, you find many companies you can buy from to suit you and your price range. They are easy to put up. You can also stack together many hoophouses to give yourself more growing room. It can grow as your business develops and grows. Let's say you bought a 16x32. You can buy another the next year and make it a 16x64 and keep adding as you need. A hoophouse is just another form a greenhouse but with a hoop design. Growing in the ground in a hoophouse that's 16 feet wide, you may be able to grow 2 or maybe three rows depending on how tall your hemp will grow. You will be limited from growing more because of the different height from the hoop. The most ideal tall space is in or near the center, which if it's a 16-foot wide greenhouse would be 8 feet tall. Growing in pots that have pans underneath to catch the run-off water will limit the available height for your plants to maybe 6-7 feet tall. The best part is hemp plants can be planted on a hill in a hoophouse.

Growing in the ground in hoophouses can help concentrate your pre-work for the soil. Instead of concentrating on fertilizing a 1-acre area, you can save money and rework an area that maybe 16x32 feet. This can allow you to produce high-quality hemp that you can grow year-round, rather than risk producing hemp that will be low quality or dead.

While we appreciate the many advantages of hoophouses, there are some disadvantages to keep in mind. Hoophouses won't keep out water runoff when growing on a hill. You can diminish this risk through digging troughs to divert water away from your hoophouse. In addition, the water can get under the plastic of the hoophouse on a hill and start removing topsoil around your plants. Moreover, hoophouses can gather extra humidity with water that doesn't run off in either a ground grown or pot-grown environment. It's better if you can control how much water it gets because your plants can still get molded in a wet environment. Most of all, you can still have pest issues in ground-grown hoophouse hemp crops; however, you will be able to control it better. Pests can also gain access inside your hoophouse. If a mole finds its way in, you will have an easier time trapping it because it will be obvious it's there. Any larger animal will be obvious because it will either dig under or break through the plastic. In that case, it will make it easier to isolate where to put the specific animal's deterrent. Even in the case of bugs, it can be eliminated easier because you can release ladybugs to eat all hemp pests, and the hoophouse will contain all of the ladybugs so that the ladybugs must feast on the pests on your hemp plants, which is the same measure you can take in a greenhouse or growhouse.

While greenhouses or any grow room can be extremely beneficial to hemp, they do come with complications. Most greenhouses have a 5-year guarantee on the cover. However, the guarantee does not cover tears acquired during assembly. On a hoophouse, the one-piece film can cost you an extra $600 if you tear it. Some don't come with the cooling system, fans, heating or the framework for those devices, so you will have to plan for the added expense. As well, if you do the frame during the building incorrectly and make a mistake on cutting the cover, it can ruin your whole setup and let outside elements in. Many don't come with the door or the framing for the door which you either have to source yourself or pay a higher price for the setup from the company. The instructions for installing your greenhouse or hoophouse isn't written in finer details, and it's not something every construction company is familiar with setting up. Without the right construction company available, this can be a setback on getting your greenhouse up and ready.

Another complication is a greenhouse or grow tent is only as clean as you make it. It won't prevent bugs if you don't have clean tools or the come through the greenhouse door as you open it. It won't prevent fungi, as their spores are everywhere. They can hitch a ride on our clothing if we have walked through weeds.

We suggest that you create a sealed door area separate from your grow room so you can change into sterilized clothing. This will allow a better control environment for your hemp. You must work with fresh gloves each time you handle your crop. If you have unwashed hands after you come from the washroom you can infect your whole crop in a matter of a day with E. coli. Using fresh gloves and practicing cleanliness will prevent you from infecting your crop and making it dangerous to the public. Gloves can prevent your hands from getting sticky from working with the resin all over the buds and leaves as well. Having a mask can be beneficial because the smell can get quite overpowering, especially in the flowing stage of growth. Smoking should be avoided in a greenhouse. Hemp can absorb the smoke and get inside the plant through the leaf.

You will have to clean the tools that you work with every day. After every use, you should wash your tools down with rubbing alcohol to disinfect them. You shouldn't mix tools that you work with hemp with other plants, especially any plants growing outside. A dirty tool can such as a water bucket, shears, trowel, boots, or even gloves infect your whole crop if they are contaminated with fungi, E.coli, or hemp-killing bugs. They should be the first place to check and clean if you start having issues with any of the above.

All in all, growing hemp flower varieties in a greenhouse or other inside structure is the best option. It protects your plants against the elements, a plethora of bugs and pests, and it is easier to control your growing environment. You have more control over the vegetative and flowering phase. Other structures, such as hoophouses and growhouses, provide an alternative to greenhouses. Each type of structure has advantages and disadvantages. The disadvantages can be discouraged through careful planning, cleanliness of the growing environment and tools used, and being present to care and watch over your plants every day.

However, as with all rural areas, many properties have a lot of land available for cultivation; hence, growing hemp in fields is the growing option many prefer. If you decide to go with this option, as with greenhouse farming, you will still have some preparing to do to prepare your land and soil for hemp's specific needs so it can grow up as healthy as your potatoes and corn. This process begins with choosing the best plot of land to accommodate your hemp crops. The items you will need to think about that will work best for your situation is in the following chapter, Chapter 5.

Hoophouse

5. PLOTTING FOR SUCCESS:
SITE ASSESSMENT FOR HEALTHY HEMP

Growing your hemp plants outside is an option many farmers wish to choose for obvious reasons. For flowering varieties, it is even more of a gamble, as expressed in the greenhouse chapter. It is like rolling the dice to see what income you'll earn, left to chance rather than highly controlled growing conditions. However, we do understand that not everyone wants to invest the money into purchasing several greenhouses, complete with thousands of buckets if they would like to grow hemp on a large scale. The availability of the land, the soil that has already been conditioned to grow other crops, and the opportunity to work this new crop into their old routines makes this an attractive option. Established farms offer the major equipment, such as seeders, that can come in handy in implementing, growing, and harvesting the hemp. If farmers concentrate on growing grain, seed, or fiber rather than high-CDB varieties, farming hemp can seem like a transition that may not be challenging to implement.

Yet, hemp has different requirements to grow healthily that are different from corn, potatoes, and tobacco. Hemp prospers when certain nutrients are present in the ground and burn when fertilizers containing certain ingredients have been implemented over many growing cycles. Your past crops may have drawn out many of the nutrients hemp needs to thrive, and hemp has a tendency of soaking up pesticides in the ground, where they will wind up in the plant in high concentrations. Whatever worked for your past crops will not work for hemp, leaving them vulnerable to the many issues that could happen to the plant.

We witnessed this with our own eyes. When we participated during the pilot program as licensed researchers and worked with many of the universities in Virginia, we acquired the hemp plants, the product from the Virginian university pilot research programs. In the universities' research, they took the hemp seeds and simply placed them into the ground without carrying out any preparation or follow up care for the plants. The outcome from this research was valuable to learn because it established a baseline of knowledge on how the plant grows in the state when farmers plant the seeds and let Mother Nature do the rest. Some of the farmers we spoke with who worked as partners with the universities to grow plants for the universities on their site and who grew the plants that we had acquired stated they did not use pesticides, and grew the plants in the natural, clay soil. One farmer stated that tomato fertilizer was used on the university's crop.

The results of the plants were as one would expect under such growing conditions. The plants grew three to four feet in height. They suffered from a cornucopia of issues, including red spiders, wasps, and aphids, all present on the plants. The fungus had worked its way into all of the leaves and many of the stems, and on plants that were affected badly, had spread to the miniscule little buds that were impregnated with seeds. 2018 did offer a wet growing season, so these problems come as no surprise. They did not identify their male plants and pull them, so their entire crop went to seed. In addition, the quality of the seeds suffered, as we found many of the bugs hiding in the buds that were responsible for boring holes into approximately 15% of the seeds.

Damaged hemp seed

For research purposes, these outcomes were extremely valuable. It demonstrated that native conditions are not present to maximize the growth of hemp to allow the plant's natural immune system to protect it from many of these issues. It will grow: it just will not grow very well.

As farmers, our intentions are different. We want to maximize every financial investment and effort we make so that at the end of the season, we can obtain a decent asking price for our crop and earn as much money as we can. Unlike corn and tobacco, you can sell every single part of your plant, from the high-CBD buds right down to its roots. The hemp plant will fulfill a number of valuable purposes in society once other markets open up. Not only does the plant contain medicinal value in CBD, but it can also provide you with paper, clothing on your back, food, an alternative plastic, and concrete and wood to build a house for your family. When you have completed your labor, you can soothe your tired, aching joints with salve made from the hemp roots. Why waste any part of the plant at all, and why grow tiny plants when it can offer so much potential?

What we learned during our time in research has prompted the discussions in these next set of chapters. We hope you find this information valuable as you plan for a successful hemp crop and growing season. The first step is finding a plot of land and soil that contains all of the features necessary for hemp to thrive and be healthy. You will have to take account the typical weather conditions in your geographic area. We will explain how weather conditions will factor into the plot you choose. We also threw in an added bonus and included ideas on how to combat typical weather conditions that can become problematic for your hemp crop. In addition, because many of the people we spoke with were tobacco farmers who were looking to convert their fields to hemp, we include a robust discussion on the effects of tobacco on your fields. We will inform you about the typical problems that you might encounter in your old tobacco field. For the next couple of chapters, we will discuss the physical location of your hemp plot and the different aspects you need to consider to prevent plant toxicity, a lack of nutrients, the pests existing in and around your plots that can harm your crop, exposure to extreme weather conditions, and erosion and leaching of nutrients from the soil. These are all of the initial considerations you will need to scout out appropriate planting sites for your hemp crop.

Selecting Your Growing Site

To grow hemp right you need planning. Making sure you have all bases covered for possible complications will prevent failure. Hemp can go through many complications that could kill the plant. There are things you have to adjust. If the house creates too much shade, you will have to move your crop away from it or plan for a smaller crop that will fit in the sunlit area. You should investigate what else could go wrong over there. The idea is that you look at the field, take in what the atmosphere is, and be able to predict what could go wrong. Preparation is key so you aren't left scrambling or losing money in the long run. Confidence to take on any issue comes with knowing you have the answer.

As part of your initial assessment of the land and weather conditions, you should keep these conditions in mind while making your seed or clone purchase. It will help to buy strong genetic seeds or clones that are hardier than standard hemp plants. You will need ones that grow faster and taller as they will need more water past seedling age.

The first step is choosing where you are going to grow. The science of finding where you will grow is just as important as growing the plant itself.

Take a scenario like this: you hire us to come and help you grow, the first thing we will do is investigate where your ideal growing conditions are, if there are any, or let you know where your next best spot is on your property and what you can do to make it work the best you can. We would look and make sure to point out any bad spots or drainage areas that would ruin your crop if you planted in the wrong area. Selecting the correct site is of paramount interest, as the wrong site can leave your plants vulnerable to hostile growing conditions. Some fields can become prone to water pooling after torrential rainstorms, which seem to be increasing in frequency and intensity. Those plants fared poorly under those conditions. Thus, observing what effects weather conditions will have on your site is a vital step in site selection. Use the following tips to guide you to select a growing site that will not become inhospitable to your plants.

Sun coverage is an easily observable aspect of choosing your growing site. In growing environments with low heat and inconsistent sun, you would strive to select the site that provides maximum sun coverage for the plants. Conversely, if you live in a hot climate, you might want to consider growing your plants on a site that offers shade for the hottest part of the day for at least part of the time. Say, for instance, you have a patch of land that the barn shades beginning at 5PM. It provides the plants with some relief from the heat and could stave off any threat of the plants dying from extremely hot conditions. It seems it can become extremely hot just about anywhere now, as heat waves are becoming more common, but you know your environment also. Hot environments should have a bit of shade to protect the plant during the hottest part of the day while avoiding bug habitat trees like Eastern Red Cedars which contain bugs that are more than happy to check out the neighboring hemp plants.

You will need an investigation period before planting. You need to see what is around and what adjustments you need to make. Let's say there is shade from a neighbor's house that will affect or benefit your crop? That house is something you can't change, but it would affect your crop if that's the only place you can plant your hemp crop.

You can pound in four fence posts to measure the corners of your field to help mark the site of where you plan to put your hemp, and then observe the conditions in that plot of land. We suggest keeping records to help you determine what your environment is going to be like and watch the sun coverage on a few plots you picked out. Note the sun coverage, time, temperature in the shade, length of time the plants would be in the sun every day, and other factors. You should take notes every day what your temperature and humidity are those days, what your wind speed is, what happens after a certain amount of rain, and where shade goes over your field at different times of the day.

To control your outdoor growing environment, you have to know what your current typical weather conditions are that will either benefit or kill your crop. Many of these potential dangers are observable.

While the weather and temperature can be unpredictable, at least the rising, setting, and position of the sun are so predictable you could set a clock to it. Also, you know your environment as well. July and August are widely known as the "dog days of summer" for a reason. Knowing how typical weather conditions transpire in your area of the world will help you take these considerations into account. If your dog days are above 85 degrees, you may want to consider checking out the available shade on your property and whether or not you would be able to capitalize on it without putting your crop at risk. However, the advantage of hot climates is the ability to begin growing seasons early. If you choose a hemp variety with a short growing season, you may be able to grow your seedlings inside in a cup during the hottest part of the summer for a second growing season if you cannot find an area that will provide the plants with some cover.

The rain is also a factor in your site selection. Rainy environments should avoid hills and growing up angled fields where water run-off will leach nutrients from your field. Those in rainy areas will also have to find a way to create drainage for controlling rainfall on hemp plants so they aren't over-watered and molded, although there are many areas in the United States that can experience a lot of rain over the summer. Rain, as was the case this past growing season, was responsible for farmers putting off planting until July. Remember those times where you were stuck inside instead of playing outside during your summer vacation? Unless you are in a dry, arid climate, rainy summers could strike at any moment. However, in regard to site selection, if your geographical area is vulnerable to periods of heavy rainfall, you should select a growing site for your hemp that offers enough drainage even during and after a heavy downpour. One good rainstorm could ruin a patch of your hemp crop if that part of the field suffers from poor drainage during those types of conditions. Even one flood can threaten the plants within that crop.

Flooded hemp plants

If your property tends to flood every season, as is common with areas that have streams and creeks meandering through them, you may want to avoid placing your crops in jeopardy in case you have a flash flood mid-season.

As well, try to avoid fields with certain physical characteristics, such as dips. Fields with dips are going to attract more water. You should avoid planting any hemp in dips as those hemp plants are already predetermined to die when you plant them in there. That water will pool up in dips, which can hurt your hemp plants. The pools will overwater certain plants and create mold. That mold will make plants unsellable as smokable or consumable products, as it will create organic components that are dangerous to our bodies. Mold can spread from a localized area to your entire crop, especially in damp, humid conditions. The mold will stunt plant growth and leave you with 2-foot plants, barely good enough for biomass. Another issue is wet plants are a weaker plant. Hemp crops in a pool of water will be better targets for bugs and have weaker immune systems to fight off infections from those bugs. The hemp plants will die from the bug bites alone and not last the full 90-day growth cycle.

Regardless of flooding, flat fields are still desirable over plots on a slope due to nutrient leaching. Flat fields are always going to be more ideal. You can always modify the drainage and have an easier time working the field in a level area. Hemp really needs a careful balance of nutrients, and if any is lost, the plants will suffer for it.

Flooded field

Another characteristic you should look for in your field is the soil content. A field that has lots of dark brown topsoil that goes down 2-3 feet deep is ideal for full growth. A rich loam soil will produce the best hemp crops. Highly nutritious dark brown soil will decrease your need for fertilizer.

Dark brown soil should still be tested ahead of time to make sure there aren't any contaminants in the soil. You will still need to apply the necessary micronutrients to your crop to ensure full growth even though most of your nutrient needs will be covered. You should still apply compost and manure to the top of tilled soil to meet nitrogen and slight phosphorus needs. High organic content is needed for hemp growth. We will explain this in detail in the soil science section.

Dark brown soil, ideal for hemp

The <u>Virginia Department of Agriculture</u> sums up site selection for hemp growing eloquently:

> To date, our preliminary data support the importance of proper field preparation and adherence to the basic principles of agricultural production. Individuals that think any field or site can be converted to hemp production are likely to be disappointed. Best yields can be expected from fields that have been in agricultural use and are properly prepared for planting. Fields with extensive seed banks from

prior years will not produce quality crops of hemp. Hemp is susceptible to drought which can put it at a competitive disadvantage with weeds. Early moisture is extremely important to get prompt germination and seedling establishment. On the other hand, too much water is deleterious to hemp production. Hemp performs best in well-drained soils.

There are other physical aspects of the land that can either hurt or harm your hemp plants. You should avoid planting in a valley or a flatland near a mountain, holler, or high-angle hill that will run off into the area. The area will fill up with water and drown the plants. Overwatering is a major danger to hemp. For example, planting hemp in the valley in the middle of two "hollers," as we call it here in Virginia, would not be a good planting site. Many times, we witnessed those areas in between the two straight-up hills fill up with up to 3 feet of water. You'd lose your whole crop in one of these scenarios. The idea might seem attractive because most of the mountains nutrients would run off into the bottom, but the water runoff will puddle and drown your crop, creating extra moisture for a weakened immune system of the hemp plant, which leaves it susceptible to bug attacks, harmful fungi, and mold. Since storms with heavy rainfall are unpredictable, you would be taking a gamble. That holler could flood at any time during the growing season.

One side of a holler

Not all properties are flat. While it's not ideal, we can work with it. The focus is to prevent some of the plants of the bottom from getting flooded while doing your best to prevent erosion from the top portion. In severe water runoff scenarios, you will want to reconsider having your plants there. If there's any danger of you topsoil eroding it will ensure you won't get a full productive growth, if it doesn't damage the hemp plant or cause mold from extra contact with water. However, you may create a trench system to take extra water and deposit it somewhere else. With no fertilizer or nutrient topsoil, your hemp may only grow small and become covered with fungi.

The importance of hemp growth is the roots extending out early in the growth cycle. Phosphorus can help with that, but it also takes time. Having the nutrients necessary for hemp growth mixed into the soil for the roots to absorb will prevent your nutrients from washing away. One of the best ways to double growth is to add the nutrients in water and water it directly around the stalk on the ground. This can help boost growth in hemp and ensure growth even if your property might lose some from water runoff.

The more severe the angle of the hill the worse the erosion may become. Sun coverage for hilly areas will also lead to uneven sunlight distribution among the plants in your crop. The direction of the hill to the sun will affect how you hemp grows as it will affect how much growing power it will get. Because hemp can have small root systems when it does not have its needed nutrition, there a chance hemp plants as old as 2 months can get washed away in water runoff and soil erosion.

For all of the reasons cited above and additional reasons, you should avoid planting your crop near a tributary, creek, or pond. A wild water source will create extra moisture and vapor and be another variable that will make it difficult to control for moist conditions. It's tempting because that can be a quick resource for watering your crop but there's always a chance of the wild water source flooding over into your crop and drowning your plants. In addition, the water source generates higher humidity, which is not a friend to your plants.

Another reason why you should be wary of planting near streams and rivers is the possibility of contamination. A stream or a river crossing from someone else's property into your own could bring contaminants with it. For example, our property includes land that has a stream that runs through the entire community. However, when we spoke with the town, they stated that the stream is not a protected water source. The cows drinking from the stream defecate into it. A neighbor released scores of Mallard ducks into the stream. They found their way downstream into Kentucky, and the local residents appreciated all of the free eggs the ducks laid along the side of the stream. People also swim in parts of the stream with easy access when the dog days become too much to bear. From this example, you can see why we wouldn't want the local stream's water finding its way into our hemp crops.

If you have a wild water source finding its way into your property, you will have to test if that wild water source has been contaminated by E. Coli, which will ruin your flowering hemp crop from which edibles are created. A wild water source could have a workup of microbials that would put consumers at risk if they ate an edible hemp product created with contaminated hemp from your property. Wild water sources could contain radon as well and make your hemp radioactive. You don't want the worst case scenario to occur and have the wild water source contaminate and drown your crop. It's best to keep your plant away from high humidity and also to test where you grow.

In addition to physical characteristics of the land that carry telltale signs of the potential to flood, you should get to know your land well enough to see where drainage is poor. This is another condition that is easy to observe, fortunately, and if you are used to working your land, using your powers of observation will help you learn where your property has poor drainage. Poor drainage is common for clay soils as is so commonly seen in the south. Even without these physical attributes, fields can contain pooled water simply because the soil's composition will not allow for easy drainage. Anywhere that water will pool from ground saturation is a danger to your hemp plant. We have experienced this with clay soil in the southern region of the U.S. One way to check for ground saturation is to see your planned field after heavy rainfall. For our experience with clay soil, it usually takes a week of consistent rainfall to soak the ground. A visible and slippery layer of water will cover over the ground. You should mark what type of soil you have and how long it takes to saturate if it does at all. That will tell you how much drainage your soil has. Drainage is paramount to growing hemp so knowing what you're dealing with before planting will tell you so you can adjust the soil to have more drainage. If you can't wait for the rain to test your soil's saturation point, you can get 1-gallon bottles to help out. You will have to get a 3-foot spot to bare soil so you can see when water starts to puddle when you dump the water over it. Keep pouring the 1-gallon bottles over the spot until the soil stops absorbing the water if you go over 15 gallons without a puddle formed you should be safe. If it does puddle before the magic number, you will have to mark it down and compare it to your annual rainfall to see how many days of rain it will take to kill your crop.

Different atmospheres benefit the same crop at different points of its lifetime. The shade is more important when your crop is still in seedling form. More darkness is needed at that point of growing, the flowering stage also requires more average darkness. Those are the first and final stages of growing. The middle stage requires more light and more sun while maintaining under 85 degrees and above 70 degrees. In that heat range, hemp will grow and not stunt. To get to its maximum height you want to grow in that range. So depending on your area you will want to plant when it's closest to that range. Planting shade trees, putting up sun barricades, or putting up tents across hot spots are in your field will help keep your plants cool. Another alternative is planting your crop near an area that has shade that will cover most of your field.

As you appraise different sites, you will want to take into account the average wind speed over your prospective site and whether or not there are any surrounding structures that can provide natural and manmade protection for your plants. A constant level of high wind can hurt your plants and cause curling to happen, especially if you're growing the less hardy flowering hemp. Checking your average wind speed is as easy as checking the weather online. Most weather channels or websites will tell you wind speed or give high wind speed warnings. If you ever watch the wind, you may notice that wind will often follow along the lay of the land. You will have to check if your planned field gets a consistent breeze or if there are points of wind natural protection or trees guarding that field. Natural wind protection comes from hills around that block that area from wind. You can have man-made protection around that could be blocking wind such as a barn. Putting up wind socks or small flags can help you see the force of the wind going along the ground of the possible plots you have chosen.

Now, you will want to appraise the surrounding natural shade providers around your plots to see if they will help or hinder your crops at different times of the growing season. If you're in a cool area, you may want to cut down any trees that give shade on your crop so you can get more sun. If your crop isn't getting enough heat to evaporate any dew on your crop, it will mold. Having shade will not help in keeping your crop balanced if you're having trouble getting enough sun.

Trees can also be used to bring shade during the hottest part of the day to save your crop from burning. You can measure how far the shade will go in your planned field and adjust your field accordingly if needed. This can be a much needed save during a hot summer that can save your plants and keep them growing.

Sycamore trees absorb water at a high rate. They can benefit your crop if you are having heavy rain and drainage problems. Sycamores grow near wet environments and look like white trees with peeling bark. Sycamores, however, can harm a crop in drought or low rain conditions and steal your crop's water, essentially killing the piece of the crop grown near the sycamore. Knowing your environment can help you use sycamore trees to your benefit.

Converting Fields from Other Agricultural Products to Hemp Plots

Cornfields, hayfields, and tobacco fields are the least ideal sites for planting hemp. Soil set up for a different crop than hemp should be kept that way. Keep your corn in your corn fields, and start fresh with a new field for your hemp crop. Growing in a tobacco field also leaves hemp vulnerable to bug attacks. The remnants of cut tobacco left after a harvest are a nested for insects that attack hemp and eat the plant. Since most tobacco fields have been used generations for tobacco, most of the nutrients are gone, leading to weaker plants, adding to the plant's vulnerability to bug attacks. For these reasons, tobacco soil has a higher amount of bugs in the soil than other soil, leading to a lower survival rate for your hemp plants. In many of the Virginian fields in our area, we see many farmers growing in fields where tobacco was grown in the previous season, and those plants are far from healthy. The plants suffer from mold and bugs that are indifferent to what type of plant you put in the field: they're happy to eat it anyway.

Instead, we recommend planting in any field that has high nitrogen, and no chemical pesticide use, while weed amount has been kept under control. In the soil science section of this book, we will explain why you should consider starting fresh rather than growing in an old tobacco field.

If you have a lot of land, you might be able to easily control for these factors. However, if you have limited land or if all of the flatlands you have available have a tendency of flooding every so often, not just in the spring, or if you have land that becomes shadowed over from your neighbor's giant barn, your options might be limited. We can't always control where we can farm, but we have to make it work by forming the earth to our needs and purposes. It takes knowing when the sun is hitting your field, how humid the air is, what type of soil you have, what may have been grown there before, what your most fertile spot on your property or growing area if you have any, what's being grown by neighbors around you, where water run-off is going, and what problem animals may be around the field. In Chapter 6, we will explain the common animals that can cause problems in your hemp fields and what to do to keep them out of your hemp fields.

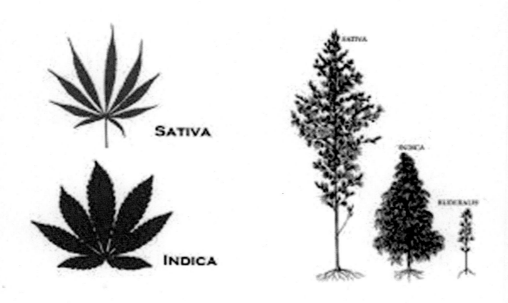

Sativa (hemp) and Indica (pot): Physical characteristics

6. SITE PREPARATION: PROTECTING YOUR CROPS FROM HOOVES AND PAWS

Animals might make good fodder for children's movies, but many wild animals are an enemy to the farmer. Some domestic and wild animals can cause problems for your hemp crop, and each can introduce pathogens that can infect your plants. In your growing site assessment, you will want to consider what neighboring wildlife you have near your hemp site.

While many problem animals can affect your crop, one of the concerns with wild animals in your crops is the introduction of E. coli in your crop. E. coli comes from fresh uncomposted manure. Deer can break into your field, attracted to the aromatic smell of hemp. We often see their hoof prints and scat in the hemp fields on the farms we consult. Deer will eat the leaves and bud from the plants, leaving the plant vulnerable to bacterial infections and a weakened immune system. Penetrating bugs can also jump from the deer onto the plant and create a myriad of other problems such as fungi and molds that can kill your plant and spread to the rest of your crop very quickly.

You will need to investigate your wild deer population. Your field may even be a feeding ground for deer. If you have deer in your field you will have to either hunt them or put up 8-foot-tall fencing that rises at least 8 feet around your whole field. You should put out tracking cameras in your field if you find if your hemp crop has been chewed on or you find deer droppings on the soil. The E.coli in the droppings can absorb into the ground and get absorbed into the hemp.

Rabbits and mice can also harm your crops and bring disease to your plants. Rabbits are difficult to get rid of and will chew on your hemp. Even if you cut the lower branches off, rabbits will chew on your stalks and open a potential infection site for bacteria and fungi. The holes rabbits can make in your crop can damage root systems which would kill the hemp plant. Mice can bring with them several bugs that will cause disease in the hemp, and mice can act as an easy taxi service for those bugs to spread throughout the crop.

If you are planting clones or seedlings in the ground, rabbits are the most dangerous at this point. It's possible for them to eat the whole plant. Over a short time you would find most of your expensive seedlings gone. Mice will chew on seedlings, and the holes in the ground created by mice might upend your seedlings from their short root systems and kill them. Once you plant your hemp, it needs to stay put, so moving it after you discover these problems is not an option. Moving the plants will stress the hemp plant and lead to its death, especially for the more delicate varieties.

Poison should be avoided for taking care of mice in your field. If the poisoned rat dies in the field it will bring dead matter that will bring on bacteria and fungi that will harm your crop. If the poisoned mouse is overlooked and absorbed into the soil that poison will absorb inside the local hemp plant(s) and cause them to be poisonous as well.

Groundhogs can cause issues with their immense systems of underground holes. The holes are known to trip up tractors, leading to injuries and deaths. They will eat the hemp plants much like rabbits and leave your hemp stressed and fighting to stay alive from bacterial infection. If you do see them you will have to plug up all their holes, send a smoke bomb in and shoot them as they come out their last hole.

Voles and moles can also be an issue. Moles can dig up your ground on the surface and damage your hemp roots. This can be especially damaging in the seedling phase as the roots can get knocked out by their tunneling. The tunnels can be as deep as a foot, which is enough to maim the roots of a young growth hemp plant. Voles will feed on your leaves, which can hurt your plants' overall growth and possibly weaken its immune system. Moles can spread bugs and parasites to your plants. You'll often find moles in moist soils with low drainage because that's where underground bugs and pests thrive for it to eat. The safest way to get rid of a mole problem without using a method that would affect your hemp crops is to put out a mole trap. You will have to put grubs in the back of the mole trap and bury it underground. After checking it every 4 hours until you catch the mole or vole, you can dispose of it as you see fit. Most other methods involve either tar, chemical poisons, or flooding the holes, which would have all bad effects on your crop. While tobacco does act as a repellent, it's not suggested for hemp to be in that field, so another solution is red cayenne pepper on top of the ground. These pests can be more difficult to get rid of, but if you are vigilant and check your plants every day, you can eventually catch them and prevent them from disturbing your hemp crop. However, domestic farm animals could also be attracted to your hemp plants.

Farm animals can also leave E. Coli in your field and/or plants if they break-in. Sheep, goats, and cows can eat the plants which would leave behind bacteria and penetrating pests from other plants they have eaten. E. coli bacteria can also be left behind from the manure.

For farm animals, you will have to reinforce your fencing to make sure they don't break out. If possible, you should try to keep your field away from your farm animals. Fencing your hemp field with either metal fencing or electric fencing will help protect the crop from animals that may escape. As goat owners, we know, when goats break through the fencing, because it happens, they always go to the place you don't want them to go and they eat all of the plants you don't want them to eat.

Thus, you will want to think about investing in some fencing. The initial investment of fences might seem a bit steep in the short run, but if you look at it as a long-term investment, it makes more sense. A ruined crop could mean a six-figure loss. In the long run, an investment in fencing for your hemp crops, especially if they are of the flowering variety, can help protect your present and future investments.

In our area, not only do we worry about furry intruders, but we worry about crop theft. Many farmers have experienced theft of their tobacco plants. In addition, humans can also contaminate crops. It's best to invest in fencing to ward out *any* intruders.

The conditions listed in Chapters 5 and 6 are not ideal, and are a regular part of the types of battles farmers of all different crops must contend with every day. Hemp, because of its delicate nature, needs to start off strong in order for its anti-weed and immunity to kick in. If it does not, the hemp becomes vulnerable to the hostilities within an environment. One more aspect of hemp farming must be taken into account: the weather. It is the element within the growing environment that can be the least cooperative. However, if you do run into hostile weather conditions, there are some solutions we have developed that can help you combat weather that will hinder the development of your plants. Chapter 7 contains these helpful details.

Possible thieves come in all shapes and sizes

7. BATTLING THE WEATHER: PREPARING FOR WEATHER CONDITIONS THAT WILL RUIN YOUR HEMP CROP

We highly suggest changing your growing environment to suit hemp if you are going to grow and make money. In not doing so, industrial hemp will be at risk of being stunted, bug-ridden, mold-ridden, and possibly toxic. The growing environment is like a little world that hemp lives in. It will give it either help in the success of hemp or the failure of the plant. This is why we suggest growing in a greenhouse where the growing conditions can be controlled and kept to consistent levels for sunlight exposure, temperature, and humidity, and minimization of bugs and pests rather than growing in the ground where in the world of Mother Nature anything could come blowing by and badly affect your plants. In addition, you will bypass the problems inherited from growing in an old tobacco field, or even outside in the sandy clay southern soil.

When you must grow a delicate plant in less-than-ideal weather conditions, you might feel like Don Quixote battling the windmill but with less optimism. Problem-solving for the weather, over which man has no control, might seem daunting, but farmers are resilient, creative people. We have provided some of that creativity here to help you combat the elements.

The good news is that there are measures you can take to prevent wind, sun, and water damage to your precious plants. Like carrying an umbrella when rain is predicted or going out to buy rock salt and sand when the weatherman forecasts snow, you can prepare for the elements you might encounter during your growing season, and there are many things you can do to prepare for the worst-case weather scenarios. In other words, we can offer advice which is more effective than battling a windmill with a broom. Consider these suggestions a starting point: you might be able to come up with your own creative solutions.

You will still have to control weather conditions to make sure your hemp plant isn't overwatered from rain, attacked by bugs, wilting from too much wind, or being burnt by the sun. Grain and hemp varieties might be a bit easier and less finicky to grow than flower varieties, but the more measures you take before your growing season to prepare for the worst of weather conditions, the better off you will be for any hemp crop. Having the correct mindset and approach helps in any scenario. It is like running a fire drill in case of fire or preparing for a natural or manmade disaster: all devastating effects can be minimized with proactive preparation. Assume the worst is going to happen, and you get to relax when it does not.

After taking care of soil you, still have to be proactive and reactive. It takes daily checking of each plant to make sure it isn't dying or has a disease that will spread through the whole crop. Barriers and roofs may have to be made in certain parts of the field to keep the hemp plants alive.

You may have to implement digging troughs as an emergency measure to prevent soil erosion and flooding of the plants in the case that a week of continuous heavy rainfall so that your plants do not drown. Troughs should be dug about 1 to 2 feet down, and hill direction should be kept in mind. You do not want the trough to put the water on another section of hemp and drown those plants. When working with hills, it would be beneficial if there's an old tributary to guide the water as well. Work the troughs around your patch of hemp plants and aim it toward the bottom of the hill. Think of a box that joins around the top and bottom ends. You can use this to bring water to drier parts of your field by drawing a path to those that need it. Using a tractor to create the trough is suggested to work efficiently.

The blazing hot sun can wilt or burn the hemp plant if the temperature is over 85 degrees Fahrenheit for too long, a common scenario in the southern states, but can easily occur in the Midwest, in the West, and in the Northeast. One way to combat the heat is creating a temporary roof to limit sun exposure to your plants. A sun barricade is essential a shade creating a wall that will cast a shadow over your crop when the sun is in the right position. It can be made of wooden pallets and held up with either PVC or fence posts sunk or hammered into the ground. The fence posts or PVC would be in between the pallets on each side to hold it up. When sturdy, it can help with wind blockage and also be used as fences to keep out animals. While this will take a lot of resources, mainly two fence posts per 4-foot pallet plus 2x4's for bracing if needed, it can benefit in casting shade and protecting from high winds. We suggest using fence posts for either side of the pallet to keep it upright, and sinking a pressure-treated 2x4 board in the ground to drill the pallet into if you are looking to make it over 1 pallet tall. The treated 2x4 would be drilled into the center of the pallet.

A great way to create an overhang is with pallets and UV protection tarps in the early stage of plant development. Because pallets are almost always 4-feet tall, that is only half the mature height of the plant. The best way to make the pallet overhang that is also cost-effective is with three sides and one side open to make sure you can access your plants while the other side helps support the tarp. They should be mounted in the ground every 4 feet with fence posts, rebar, or PVC inside the pallets to hold them up. You can use fence wire to twist around the mounting pole and the pallets to hold them in place. Use clamps to mount the tarp so that it is removable. The sides should be mounted with 90-degree brackets every foot that can hold 2 screws per side. The other option is PVC pipe mounted 2 feet into the ground at four points with clamps that sit around the patch that needs sun protection. You must be aware of the fact that the tarps can trap moisture and increase the humidity. We suggest monitoring your plants' environment with a Hydrogro meter so that you can measure humidity at all times under the tarp.

Each structure has its strengths and can be helpful when you want to prevent certain problems from occurring. The advantage of PVC is that you can reach higher up with the tarp so it can be used longer and for older plants. However, it will not work as a barricade. Pallets work well as barricades if wind causes the leaves to twist and wilt. A high wind environment can also wind damage your crops. Under constant wind, your hemp plants can get windburn. The fan leaves will curl which will eventually lead to those leaves dying off. With those leaves compromised the plant will get less light. Whichever technique you choose to employ, having these structures in place will help you react with immediacy so that you are not rushing to install these structures when you need them most. Also, you have to design your temporary roofs with your unique property characteristics in mind.

You should also strive to control the amount of water that is left on the plant itself after long periods of rainfall. Rainfall left on the plants combined with dew and/or saturated environments will lead to molded plants very quickly. Wet growing seasons have been known to cause problems in hemp plants. In North Carolina, this wet growing season caused <u>fungi</u> and <u>root rot</u> in their crops for the season. Large fans should be placed at four corners pointing inward on each field can help dry off sodden plants. This will dry off excess water and the intersection of the air will help dry hemp plants in the center.

Watch out with placing the fans too close to the outside layer of hemp. It is possible to wind damage your hemp, which will prevent growth and wilt the plant, which will lead to the eventual death of the plant. We've experienced this with mini fans in grow tents. The small amount of wind bounced around and wilted a plant. It took about a month to set the plant back to normal growth, but the plant did not grow to full size in that experiment and many leaves curled. The fans with 3-4 foot diameters should be at least 5 feet back so outer plants don't get damaged. Only the lowest setting should be used so you don't simulate a hurricane in your crop.

Heaters can also be used in unison to help dry the plants. If your inner field plants aren't getting enough air to dry them or you are worried about certain ones, heaters can be used for short periods to help dry your plants before night time saturation occurs. We do suggest combining them with fan use as trying to use only heaters on your full crop would be very expensive. Placement is also an issue because you don't want to burn your hemp plants from being in direct contact with the heaters.

We highly suggest only using fans and/heaters during the hottest part of the day and leaving the electric on a timer. In case of sudden rain, the last thing you want is a fire hazard in your crop so you will have to keep a close eye on the plants and your weather conditions. Keeping watch will also help in case you need to adjust your fan or heater position for other plants. You should also keep a shed or storage building for your fans nearby so they don't rust or fall apart being left out in the rain. Heaters are a major fire hazard out in the rain, so it is important to keep an eye on it, put them in a safe spot where it won't burn your plants but won't short or spark. You should take extreme care, as these items cannot be submerged or come into contact with water. Work wisely when it comes to electrical appliances and moisture.

If it is a cool or cold environment, you will have to run cords or electric for only heaters instead of fans. The fans will generate cool air and during wet environments will create cold weather mildew which can ruin your crops completely. The southern region of the U. S. is also known for high humidity, which can create mold issues in hemp if it is over 85% at any length of time. There are points in when 80% average humidity is necessary for growth in hemp. In contrast, levels above 85% humidity puts your hemp at risk of mold and possibly turning male and sending your whole crop to seed instead of bud. High humidity also promotes high microbial (microviruses, fungi, and yeast) growth. Mildew can stunt your hemp plants and eventually kill them.

Mold

In the last chapter, we expressed the importance of good farming soil on your plots. Even well-farmed soil can have drainage problems, as is seen in many southern areas with lots of clay in the soil. If you do decide to convert your tobacco fields, or if you are growing in the south and decide to grow hemp in your clay fields, we recommend taking the trouble preparing your soil so that your hemp plants can prosper to protect your investment and future profits. Depending on the condition of your topsoil, you may have to dig up the ground and lay over new dark topsoil to make your hemp grow well. To make up for sandy soil you will have to dig up the soil more than the maximum root depth to make sure the roots can get the necessary nutrients. Clay soil has <u>poor drainage</u> and can drown your plants. We suggest digging out your new hemp-growing field at least 20 inches down to fill in new topsoil fitted to hemp. It will take a dump truck or more to refill in your field depending on how many acres you are planting.

Ingenuity, modern means, and changing your fields to suit your hemp plants can help combat even growing conditions that we cannot control. We cannot control the weather, but we can develop strategies to help combat problems that arise when they do occur.

Once you have selected your sites, you can spend the earliest part of the growing season preparing the site and all of the additional measures so they are ready to go so you can do all you can do to save your plants against pests and hostile conditions. You can begin this as soon as the snow melts, if you have snow, and the ground defrosts. Next, you will have to decide on which strain to grow. When you order seeds, they might take some time to arrive. Also, because there are so many varieties of industrial hemp, you will have to decide what types of seeds to obtain. Part III will give you information that will help you decide what strain to grow.

Part III

Planning II: Choosing Your Strains for the Hemp Product You Want

Hemp buds

8. CHOOSING THE RIGHT SEEDS CAN MEAN THE DIFFERENCE BETWEEN FLOWERS AND ROPES

As established earlier in this book, there are many varieties of hemp seeds. In this chapter, you will learn those varieties, what types of products are typically yielded from these varieties, and the availability of these types of seeds in the United States. You will also learn the complications you can experience with the seed supply available in the United States.

Different Strains

Hemp has many strains all concentrating on a certain industry. You can get a strain with either increased stalk size (fiber), increased seed output (seed), higher CBD amounts (flower), or higher THC amounts in marijuana-legal states (hybrid). Strains like Cherry Wine and Berry Blossom concentrate on "High CBD" and larger flower output. Fibranova is an Italian seed variety that is concentrated on fiber and increased stalks. Tygra is a seed variety that concentrates on high seed production. Many hybrids exist that have high THC and come from states where marijuana is legal, such as Colorado and Oregon. We recommend avoiding all strains and varieties if your state has not legalized marijuana or if you do not yet have the appropriate licenses to grow marijuana.

Differences of Each Strain

Grain can be sold in seed form for either other growers to make mash, make hemp oil, or hemp flour. Of course, you must be able to pick out the rest of the seed, which requires expensive industrial machinery that tears the plant apart. Some states may need you to get a processors' license to pick the seeds from the bud. Fiber has many industries and only requires you to grow it as tall as possible. It will need to be cut and dried properly so that it can be as sellable as possible. Fiber carries the least risk because the strains have been developed over generations to produce plants with low THC.

Flower is the most volatile market and competitive. When growing hemp flower you will be mostly selling to CBD oil makers. Flower can be sold as pure bud but you have to compete with marijuana-legal states in that regard. Buds would have to be seedless and plentiful for profit to be made. Most standard hemp plans can produce approximately ¾ a pound dry weight, which can be sold at a gram price. After buds are separated and sold, with a processing license, you can sell the rest of the plant for grain and fiber. Flower selling is a different way of growing hemp that must be preplanned. You have to spread the plants wider apart, meaning fewer plants to grow. Most seed and fiber companies are looking for large quantities, in the quarter-ton to ton range. However, there could be smaller companies who will take less. While growing fiber it is possible to grow legal bud that you can sell, but make sure to do it legally. Despite the benefits of flower varieties, many legal authorities are not looking for flower to be legal. Thus, it may not be a permanent market due to the many lies and scams. At this moment, they get away with it because of the lack of regulation. Many cases growers lie on their CBD and THC amount and use fake tests which hurt the whole market because most of that hemp flower is over the 0.3% legal limit. This hurts the whole industry, especially growers who take the care to grow a legal product. Because of the concern for consumer safety, many states discourage the growth of flower varieties of hemp with high CBD. This will be explained further in Chapter 6.

The strains from Europe, China, and Canada are mostly grain and fiber varieties that help grow tall hemp plants and broad bases. In addition, most of them have been bred to contain a THC level of 0.20% and low CBD levels, usually hovering around 1-2%.. There are only certain hemp varieties that have been approved to grow in Europe.[1] The market outlets for such crops are more well-developed than in the United States. On the other hand, the largest hemp market in the United States is the CBD market. The hemp strains in this market contain high CBD, and hopefully, low THC.

As recent as a year ago, seeds were extremely expensive and difficult to obtain. Clone farms wanted thousands and thousands of dollars to even obtain a hundred clones. This situation has improved. Yet, there are certain caveats farmers must be aware of so you can avoid many of the typical mistakes we see farmers committing all of the time, and we are waiting for the other shoe to drop when the legality of their crop comes into question, all because they do not know their hemp strains. Or, they are suckered into buying the wrong hemp strain for what they wanted and their initial investment is lost along with any of the possible earnings.

Take, for example, a farmer in Minnesota who bought clones from a Colorado company. Not only did a significant portion of the clones go male, something the farmer was guaranteed would not happen, but the CBD level was only 1.5% when he thought he had purchased clones with high CBD. If he had learned his hemp strains and became an educated consumer, he might have been able to avoid the financial loss. This section will help you from falling into the same trap.

---

[1] These are the hemp varieties that growers can grow in Europe: Armanca, Asso, Beniko, Bialobrzeskie, Cannakomp, Carma, Carmagnola, Chamaeleon, Codimono, CS, Delta-405, Delta-llosa, Denise, Dioica 88, Epsilon 68, Fedora 17, Fédrina 74, Felina 32, Félina 34, Ferimon – Férimon, Férimon 12, Fibranova, Fibrimor, Fibrol, Finola, Futura 75, Futura 77, KC Dora, Kompolti, Kompolti hybrid TC, Lipko, Lovrin 110, Monoica, Red petiole, Santhica 23, Santhica 27, Santhica 70, Silesia, Silvana, Szarvasi, Tiborszallasi, Tisza, Tygra, Uniko B, Uso-31, Wielkopski, and Zenit.

Not just any seed or clone is going to work for your crop. The most expensive seeds aren't always going to give you a better crop, and cheap seeds may not even be hemp seeds if you didn't buy it from someone reputable.

There are a lot of different strains with different names. You have to ask yourself, "What am I going to grow?" Knowing the names of well-developed strains will help you from buying a marijuana plant by mistake, or the wrong seed for the wrong crop. If you end up growing marijuana in a hemp only state, you could get arrested depending on your state's laws. At the very least, you could be forced to pay extra lab testing fees to test your crop a second time or burn down your entire crop.

While tobacco strains will give you different strengths in growing and purposes for selling in the tobacco industry, hemp strains have a placement in different industries. Choosing a strain in hemp chooses an industry to pursue and sell to while tobacco is only regulated to the smoking, vaping, and chewing products. Choosing your seeds should be a careful process as fiber seeds are meant for tall growth, low CBD, and has very little use in the bud industry. Grain would be a bad choice for the bud industry because seedy buds sell for only $2 a bud if you are lucky, and grain is meant to produce a lot of seed per plant so that it can produce seed oil. Flower strains would be bad for fiber production because the flower strain would produce more buds rather than the fiber of the stalk. To ensure you're growing the right crop, it's important knowing the specific strain names and what their names are. We have some preliminary information for you here to get you started.

Fiber seeds

As explained in earlier chapters, fiber varieties of hemp have many applications in industries that have yet to be more fully developed in the United States. The most well-developed fiber seeds come from Italy and China. However, it can be hard getting a hold of reputable seeds. If you are looking for full growth with low CBD and 0.1% THC, Fibranova would be a good choice. Fiber can be planted within 6-7 inches of each other in a row to help obtain more fiber per acre, and planting them close together provides good weed coverage so other competing plants do not have a chance to grow and hog all of the sunlight from your crop. Europe and China have been producing fiber hemp for many years, so they come from well-developed strains that provide consistent results. Chinese and Italian strains were used in the pilot programs in many universities across the United States between 2014 and 2018. A Chinese variety of fiber-producing hemp is HanMa, which has low THC and low CBD. A higher CBD strain out of Italy is Carmagnola, which is good for both high CBD of approximately 15% on average and fiber. Hemp varieties like these are attractive because they can produce more than one type of market.

Grain Seeds

Grain can produce more seed than the other varieties and male plants don't matter in fields of grain because males will help the females produce more seed. The seed crops produce hemp seed oil or flour. The seed oil can be used as cooking oil, protein shots, lantern oil, and skin products, while the flour of the seed can be used as an alternative to wheat flour. The seed by itself can be eaten. One American grain strain is X-59 while a Polish, grain-specific strain, a bit more difficult to obtain, is Tygra. One of the benefits of seed growing is CBD amount doesn't matter as you are only harvesting the seeds. When your goal is to produce seed, you want a few males, but not so many that it cuts down on your profits. This type of seed is a consumable product, so care should be taken to check your soil to see if the ground is toxic, as the case may be with old tobacco fields. The seeds will absorb as much of the hemp plant's nutrients amount as it can and will bring in any microbial and radioactive element that the hemp plant has sucked through the ground. Hemp seeds are also susceptible to fungi and microbial rot.

Flower Seeds

Flower strains refer to high CBD hemp plants where the concentration is on growing big flowers/buds. It is very competitive and everyone wants to get into it. When done right, which is usually greenhouse-grown for maximum growth, it will go for a high price per bud. Yet, you should keep in mind that growing flower varieties in fields is the riskiest strain to grow. In addition, bud growing is the most labor-intensive crop because of its delicacy and must be monitored closely so you can produce high levels of CBD while keeping the THC levels low and not allow male plants to germinate your buds and make your crop go to seed. Also, because flower is most often created into a consumable product, which is either turned into oil or smokables, if your plants suffer from any fungus, bacteria, or other issues that a poor growing site or conditions could introduce into your crop, it will make the purchasing of your plants highly unlikely due to safety issues.

One of the best known and most reliable strains of flower is Cherry Wine. It is a 0.2% on THC and 8%-16% CBD. Most growers we consult for plant or bought Cherry Wine, and many sellers/dispensaries even go as far as to fake fiber strain grown (Fibranova) buds as Cherry Wine. One complaint we have gotten on Cherry Wine is when it's field-grown, it has a high propensity to go hot, often forcing full crops to be burned down. Another common flower strain is Berry Blossom. It is a strain that comes in at a 0.2% to 0.3% THC while CBD is high from 10% to 15%.

The next most mentionable strain is AC/DC. It smaller and bushy plant with auto-flowering potential. It has high CBD at 17% and very little THC at 0.09%. It comes from the Euro/Asian type of cannabis called ruderalis, an auto-flowering tiny cannabis plant. These seeds are very expensive and rare to find, but their buds also go for a lot of money. This hemp strain would be safe for the GC method states (see the Understanding your Labs chapter for a full explanation). It is technically a hybrid because it contains a mix of two different hemp species, but they do not have high THC.

Special Sauce is another high-flower, high-CBD strain. From our experience, this would be bad in a total THC method states. A Total THC report on one we investigated had a 0.7% total THC, with an actual number of 0.28% of delta-9. We explain this issue fully in Chapter 14 to arm you with the knowledge you will need to see if your state will follow total THC to determine the legality of the hemp you are growing or abide by the 2018 Farm Bill.

The Delta-9 Monkey on hemp growers' back

We suggest that you read through that chapter before you settle on buying a flower variety. It will help you determine if your state is hostile to flower varieties or if you can legally grow these strains in your state.

Ruderalis

Ruderalis is an auto-flowering cannabis plant. It's not hemp and it's not marijuana. It is a cousin species that grow in cold environments and wild in Eastern Europe. It has the ability to auto flower, meaning it does not depend on light to go into flowering stage. Ruderalis will flower on its own after 90 days regardless of the season. It is a very high CBD at 15% to 20% with very little THC. The downside, its height at maturity is very short. In a field scenario, it would get dominated by taller weeds very quickly. Yet, it would benefit in a field scenario where you can farm acres of it to be able to make a lot of money. In a greenhouse, you will have to make this species go to its maximum width and yield. Ruderalis is very usually very expensive to get a hold of but provides high CBD buds.

Hybrids

Simply put, hybrids are cannabis cross-breeds, mainly with marijuana and hemp that offer high THC and high CBD, which is not a good combination for hemp-only states. Hybrids always go over both delta-9 testing and total THC testing. In total, they are marijuana with CBD added. Most hybrids aren't legal to grow in hemp states. They are in fact pot because they are bred to contain the highest levels of both THC and CBD possible.

Hybrids will most often look closer to marijuana than hemp. They are hedge-like and bushy, and they grow wide rather like marijuana. Hemp will grow upward and looks almost like the Charlie Brown Christmas tree in the way the stalks go out. Hybrids do not make suitable plants to grow both CBD and fiber. Buds on hybrids are essentially marijuana buds. Seeds for growing shouldn't be sold to hemp-only states because those people would then be growing pot illegally ad possibly without realizing it. If you are buying seeds, it might be best to avoid buying in marijuana-legal states.

We have consulted farmers who had bought from marijuana-legal states and were, indeed, fooled into buying a strain that went hot because they did not know that they were buying a hybrid strain. It's a big issue. This issue happens because they are falsely told by growers and sellers in duel cannabis states like Colorado, California, and Oregon that it is industrial hemp when it is, in fact, marijuana. It is misinformation spread around by those sellers to make a sale, even if it puts the person buying it at risk. It's either created by the seller's ignorance of or outright ignoring the buyer's state laws. We do encourage you to check your local state's laws as a buyer to know what are they defining as legal hemp.

Hybrids are very common because in dual-cannabis states, the lines between the two are blurred. There are many online markets that make the purchase of them convenient and possible. A simple internet search will bring up several pages looking to sell hybrid clones or seeds to sell off their state surplus. Many Colorado and Oregon websites don't list their THC value or give an official lab qualifying that it is a legal delta-9 plant, so buyer beware. The best way to tell a hybrid out is if it says both "Indica" which is a name for marijuana, and also saying "hemp." For example "Industrial hemp: high CBD! Strain: Indica": Indica=marijuana.

To help you escape the trap of growing an illegal crop by mistake we will reveal to you some common hybrid names that we hear very often from growers we talk to. Many of the growers we consult don't even know that they had been growing marijuana and not hemp. One of the growers we worked with even planted 26 acres of hybrids in a hemp only state!

Trump. Trump, or T1/T2 as it is also called, are very common hybrids bought countrywide. Based on a CBD amount of 20% T1s THC is 0.62%, nearly double the legal hemp limit. T2, also known as Presidential, is much lower in CBD amount at 16% but still would produce 0.5% on the same 32:1 CBD to THC ratio as T1's.

There is also the risk that most hybrids are low generation. Unstable genetics mean that there is a 50/50 chance that it will get either parent's quality. T2 meaning the combination of two Trumps in a low generation count of under 20 will be unstable and can produce hot numbers that make it illegal. It is possible to get legal-limit plants in the mix if it were combined with a low THC hemp plant; however, there would be a 75% chance that it would turn out hot and ruin your crop.

T-1

BaOx. BaOx is another notable hybrid planted across the country. One lie often repeated about this plant is that the seeds and clones are fully feminized, even though there isn't any existing proof that efforts have been made to fully feminize the seed, meaning you could get a 60/40 chance of males/females. Based on our experiences there has been an oddly high number of males in BaOx fields. It originates from Hindu Kush and Otto lines which are both marijuana strains with high THC and no sign of hemp in its genetics, meaning it will always come over the legal THC limit.

The last thing we should mention that if the hybrid you are looking to buy has any Kush, Haze, and/or Otto in it, it could go illegal. Indica-heavy or leaning hybrid strains could be up to 30% THC, 100x the legal limit of a hemp only state. This should be taken into account when buying seeds, as early or undeveloped strains mixed with a marijuana plant can go hot in any plant, and may very well be the answer to why so many harmless flower strains go hot from one plant to another legal to another in the same field. Undeveloped strains can come from anyone who mistook it for hemp and had it in their field breeding with their hemp, and genetic of those seeds must be taken into account before buying them. Reputable is only a title deserved if the seed grower can show you proof that it is actual hemp with generations of pure hemp behind it. A marijuana plant in a hemp plant's close ancestry will then make it possible for a child of that plant to produce a marijuana plant.

The most reprehensible aspect of this discussion is the fact that many of the seed suppliers in marijuana-legal states will sell you the hybrid seeds with no care of the legal trouble it will put you in or the financial loss it will produce for your farm. We have spoken with many of these suppliers out of California, Colorado, and Oregon ourselves. They pressed us to buy the hybrid strains, and even lied to us about the potential THC level of the seed when we inquired. Luckily, because we went into it knowing our strains, we were able to learn which seed suppliers were trustworthy and which ones we should avoid because of their dubious claims.

Buying Clones to Start Your Hemp Farm

Many growers do not feel like planting their seeds in cups and waiting 2-3 weeks and transferring them to the ground after they've gotten their five sets of leaves. They opt for ordering clones by the hundreds to thousands. The clones have to either be transported by you or shipped by the flatbed. While it's cheaper to grow a crop from seed, beginning with clones can seem like an attractive option and save planting time because you are receiving a healthy batch of plants that were started either indoors or in a greenhouse. The clones have already been bred with certain genetics and are past the point when they can be very vulnerable to their surroundings. It allows you to start planting ASAP with relatively healthy plants through transplanting.

Clones are more labor-intensive. Whereas farmers can plant seeds right into the ground using typical farming equipment, clones must be planted one-by-one by hand. If you are planting scores or even hundreds of acres, it could take weeks to fill the field by hand. Unless you hire help, you might lose some of your clones if you cannot get them into the ground in time.

Clones tend to be very expensive compared to seeds. Some strains can run $10 a clone compared to $30 for a pound bag of seeds in fiber terms. You will be paying a lot more than that if you are planting flower strains. Your initial investment will be higher, which makes it a bit riskier if your crop fails due to the possible growing conditions discussed in previous chapters. In addition, many of the people supplying clones overcharge farmers. They have a minimum purchase amount and include "consultation" when you pay them at least four figures to purchase their clones. Steer clear of these people. They often do not have the expertise they claim and are simply taking advantage of farmers because of poor seed supply in the United States. A fuller discussion of typical industry scams will be covered in a future book in this series.

It makes more sense to purchase seeds and use a standard seeder to fill a field. Clones work better on a small scale if you are doing flower strains in a greenhouse, where you just have to replant them in bigger pots. However, as with our discussion of the different seed strains, you will have to be careful. You will need to purchase from a reputable clone farm growing a legal variety and the strain that will produce the product you are striving to grow.

Common Issues with Seeds and Clones

Since regulations for the hemp industry have not been fully established in a volatile marketplace, there are certain caveats that farmers must be aware of so they do not lose thousands of dollars for products that you think you're buying.

First-generation Strains. One big complication with buying your crop is inconsistent genetic from first-generation strains. Growers are constantly mixing strain to make the new super strain with the highest CBD and lowest THC. This leads to a lot of people trying to capitalize on the demand for it by doing it themselves and then selling the next generation after they mix two cannabis plants for the first time. They coin a name and sell a product that isn't going to have consistent outcomes. This is a big issue with both seeds and clones. Seed sellers will sell the seeds of their first-time crop as a new strain and run it with appealing words. Overexcited growers might work in cloning as well by snipping off the tops of their plants and selling them as clones after they grow roots from a solution. Some might sell the seeds not knowing what germinated it if they had several different kinds of cannabis in their field. The type might be Cherry Wine and BaOx or Cherry wine and Berry Blossom, but those types of sellers really wouldn't know and would promote it as them either way. They might say it's a second generation of Cherry Wine, thinking that a Cherry Wine in their field went male and made that plant. It might be all the options with each male plant germinating a different part of that mother plant, essentially meaning they are selling people different hemp hybrid seeds from the same plant. A completely different scenario can happen when a neighbor marijuana grower's plants went to male and germinated the hemp seeds that the person is trying to sell. It would be beyond their knowledge that they are selling you an unstable genetic strain of marijuana.

Weak genes make weak plants. One issue you have to watch out for is first-generation and hybrid strains can have weak bug and mold resistance. You essentially take an already fragile, temperamental plant that can make even more fragile, temperamental descendents. It may develop even more vulnerabilities due to genetic variation. A well-established breed is a 15th generation hemp plant will have more immunity to things that could potentially kill a standard one or an experimental first-generation strain. You want to make sure to grow only strong genetic, almost pure-bred hemp to give yourself the most resilient crop. If you want to develop your own seed hybrid, make sure you grow it for at least seven generations before offering it, and you'll gain a good reputation because of your plants' good results that will help growers gain great CBD levels and come within legal THC limits.

Inconsistent Naming. Another issue with picking out your crop of choice is inconsistent naming. The same strain may go under different names or the same strain may be developed in parallel but have slight differences and still be called the same name. For example, you have original Cherry Wine, then you could have a genetically unstable baby of Cherry Wine and Trump that a seller also calls Cherry Wine. It's not the original strain with better DNA, but an offshoot from that plant.

Other times people will outright say something with similar CBD levels is the one with that name when it isn't. Let's say Special Sauce comes out just like ACDC in numbers in some way, that person may just outright call it ACDC, even if it won't auto-flower. If you grew those seeds or clones you wouldn't know until 90 days later, right around flowering time. Those Special Sauce seeds or clones might have had a Kush or Ruderalis mix, but that also means it's going to have inconsistent genetics and each plant that comes from that batch of seeds or container of clones will be different from one another. Some will be hot other will be much lower in CBD then they were supposed to be, and this will lower the amount of plants that will produce the results you are seeking.

Think of genetics like a bunch of blocks piled together. Strong genetics are like Lego™ bricks. They stick together and can stand independently. Now think of weak genetics as rocks of all different shapes trying to balance onto each other. Those rocks will fall and each time you rebuild that tower of rocks it will be in a different formation with different rocks on each level. Those rocks are the inconsistent genetics that can't stand on their own and will be different a new plant is made from them.

One option you can take is to do a DNA search through Phylos to find out the strain your potential crop is. They can tell you what genes and different types of cannabis your hemp comes from. Their tests are usually about $350, but it's a necessary test if you are unsure about your crop. They will need 2 grams of plant material, and you will get your results within a month. We actually offer this service as a partner with Phylos, so you can send us your sample, and we will take care of it for you. We will provide you with our contact information to help you establish your account and prepare your sample for analysis.

"Feminized" Seeds. Another big issue is if you're looking for flower is feminized seeds commonly turn into hermaphrodites. A hermaphrodite is a plant that has both male and female parts on the same plant. No seed is purely feminized and anyone telling you that is lying. A big issue in hemp crops we visit is hermaphrodites appearing in crops. The growers believe the seed suppliers and clone farmers and believe that all of their seeds and clones will all produce female plants. In addition, they will not take the time to learn what male plants look like and ignore the males when they reach maturity and open up their pollen sacs and pollinate all of your females and cause them all to go to seed. This ruins a flower crop, and most people don't know this is something that can happen on hemp. You must be in your fields checking through them every day during flowering to look for male sacks so you can preen them off. We suggest storing male hemp sacks in nonporous containers when you take them off, and also to get to them early before they are ready to spread pollen as if you take them off during pollination the pollen will spray out and carry across your field and infect it anyway. Then, you should remove all male plants from your field. If you leave them in the field, their pollen sacs can grow back. We learned this little factoid when we ran an experiment to see if we could keep a male plant. If you have flowering varieties, the answer is a resounding no. Removing males and hermaphrodites early will help you protect your precious flowering female plants.

Issues with Seeds. One issue we've tested on is the growth rate in hemp seeds is awful. Many seed sellers do not guarantee the growth of their seeds and make you buy at your own risk. We found through testing and experiments the growth rate of the hemp seeds to be as low as 1 out of every 25. It is suggested that you plant <u>40-60 pounds</u> per acre for a growing field as many will not grow or fail at the seed level.

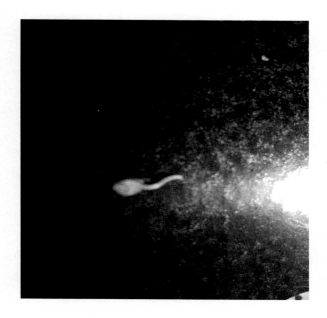

Hemp seed sprouted root

Fake Reports. From our experience, the online marketplace is full of people posting fake reports by stealing them online. One website many go to look for the stock for their crop is Kush.com. It can be a resource, but to protect yourself against fake reports, it is best to have Google Image Reverse available to spot out the fakers. Always ask for an official lab report before buying, and if they don't have it, do not buy. Many prices can be quite cheap there, but it's usually because there's usually something wrong with the products and you're taking a big risk when buying without a lab.

Wish.com from China offers hemp seed, but many growers we've spoken with run into quality control issues. It is tempting to buy from this site because of surprisingly cheap prices, but you will often not get your shipment of seeds in time. It takes 3 weeks to 2 months for suppliers to ship the seeds. Many people who grew with seeds hoping for genuine fiber had gotten house plant seeds instead. The ones that did come in with hemp either rotted, didn't grow, or had severely inconsistent genetics.

If you find an unfamiliar hemp strain from Colorado, be smart and get information on it first. Look up the THC amount. In a total THC state you are looking for 0.21% and under. If they aren't going to give a lab report from its parent crop during harvest, don't buy. Always get COAs. COA refers to the Certificate of Authenticity in the form of a genuine lab report. Also, find out what generation the plant is and if the clone field is outside or in a greenhouse. A greenhouse would be preferable because males can be better controlled in there.

Plant Infections. It is also possible that the clones or seeds you buy are already infected by microbials and mycotoxin. Microbials are often overlooked due to the fact that states often do not have testing for them as a legal requirement even though the flower products are highly consumable products. Any crop that has been infected by fungi, or mold, is immediately a dangerous crop that someone may not know they have. If those seeds are planted in the ground your field and crop will be ruined by infecting Aspergillus and Fusarium fungi. We will extend this discussion in the soil science section. Good seeds usually have strong genetics that makes it harder for the fungi to creep up from the roots. So, always get seeds from a reputable source.

Monopolies and High Prices. The last issue in picking out your crop is that companies have created monopolies on clones and seeds. At the moment, one place in Kentucky owns this country's' right to distribute European fiber seeds. Prices will be higher because of a lack of competition. Many places make you sign disclosures not to clone or make your plant go to seed from their clones and seeds they sell you. This clause is almost comical considering how easily hemp goes to seed. Many people are looking to take over the cloning industries in each state and force the buyer to buy bulk or buy none. One company we have spoken to attempted to force us to pay a $1000 consulting fee before he sold us clones, we still had to pay for clones after that. He was the only man in the state producing clones and was able to get away with it because of no legal ramifications from the state board.

Hemp in Comparison to Tobacco

Tobacco has a very good growth rate per seed while hemp has a 1 out of 20 growing rate. It becomes expensive to buy seed to grow because of the sheer volume you need per acre to get a full crop. One ton can cost up to $3000, and buying a pound at a time can cost $7 per pound even for fiber varieties, and often cost more for CBD varieties. Using a seeder to mass plant the seeds is recommended. However, you can grow a male and number of females of good genes and make your own ton of seeds to grow on a large scale.

In hemp, choosing the right strain is an important factor so you can grow the type of crop you want. In tobacco, taste and quality depends on what you do to the plant during growing and after cutting. In hemp, it is dependent on the type of hemp that you grow. Some strains are cultivated for thick stalks, which is better for paper, fiber, and rope, some for seed, and some for producing high flower for its higher CBD percentage. Picking the right one to grow is essential to success. You will be disappointed if you choose any old hemp seed and expect to grow a high CBD plant only to find that you chose hemp that is used for grain production with low CBD.

Hemp growth is also dependent on the mother plant's DNA that is passed onto the seed. If the mother plant was a small, slow-growing, weak plant so will be the child. Some seed suppliers claim that seeds are feminized, meaning that the female aspect of the plant is encouraged and the male expression discouraged. However, that is never guaranteed, and you won't get your money back if they turn out male. Feminized seed goes for more money because of the risk of what a male plant can bring, but you will be paying about $120 per 10 seeds, and in the end, you might get a male anyway.

THC is another risk factor, especially if the seed comes from states that legalized pot. There are many hybrids on the market that produce both high THC and high CBD. If THC is higher than .30, the state will consider it pot and can either get you arrested or your license revoked if it occurs with frequency. The DEA will not care if you were duped into buying the wrong seeds. It is important beyond the seller's word to make sure you don't buy seeds where the mother went over 0.30 THC and went hot. Hot plants are allowed in Colorado where hybrids of hemp and marijuana are made and sold. Hybrid growers in Colorado do not care about other state laws and several times lied to us to make a sale. It is important that you get lab tests on what THC came back with and that it matches the standard set by the Farm Bill of 2018 of delta-9 THC. Also, you should be aware that many scam artists use lab reports they procured from the internet to provide you with a false lab report that seems legitimate, so make sure that you use an image reverse search program such as Google or Tineye to make sure the person selling you your hemp product isn't deceiving you. In a separate book, we will cover scams in the hemp industry which we suggest picking up so that you can protect yourself from all deceitful practices and scams.

Hemp is still a frontier while tobacco is set in its ways; because of this, caution must be taken when purchasing seeds. Tobacco's growing tactics are widely known and practiced, and the seeds contain genes developed over generations of growing seasons. Hemp does not. A lot of seeds out on the market are first- generation wonders and could grow in any possible way. Many different varieties are being grown but have no set genetics and could go hot on a moment's notice. Many growing styles for hemp are recently developed while tobacco has a set way that works. A lot of people put out misinformation because the general public does not know how to grow hemp and believes it can be grown like any other plant. Hemp is different because you need a license to legally grow it, and you must keep the grown plant to grow within legal limits to meet strict state and federal regulations. Many who do grow it don't know how to grow it correctly or in a way to maximize the amount of money they make. Many will lose a lot of money from not being able to figure out how to make the plant succeed on a large crop level.

Thus, at this point of the young hemp industry, the mantra is buyer beware. It is important to be aware that hemp strains and varieties are grown for specific purposes, and you may not be able to capitalize on more than one function for the plant. Some strains that have been bred for many generations do contain the coveted high CBD, but many have very low CBD. Some strains can be grown for more than one purpose, but some are bred specifically to produce a crop yield that will allow farmers to capitalize on that industry, such as grain and fiber varieties. The European, Canadian, and Chinese varieties are mostly of the grain and fiber variety. Some varieties are available in the United States from abroad, but some have a monopoly on the seed supply. There are some strains that have high CBD, the most developed market in the U. S., but there are many types of hybrid strains from pot-legal states that are bred for high CBD and THC. In addition, because there are not many regulations at this point, a lot of people take advantage of farmers who are not able to identify the differences between pot strains and hemp strains. In addition, if you buy clones, they can present their own set of issues. Based on our experience in investigating most of the supply of seed and clone in the United States, our conclusion is to be careful and know your strains. When you learn the strains, make sure that your suppliers can back up their claims with legitimate lab paperwork.

Hemp seeds

In Part IV, it is time to get into the nitty gritty. Soon, the FDA and the USDA will put out regulations to make consumables safe for the consumer. At the present time, farmers are already experiencing this sentiment: farmers are not allowed to use typical herbicides and pesticides on their plants. The safety of hemp as a consumable has already been brought to the attention of the media. In addition, hemp is known for its sponge-like qualities: it drinks up everything from the soil, meaning that it is especially vulnerable to toxicity in the soil, especially if there is toxicity left over from tobacco crops. You will learn the types of issues that can typically occur in the soil due to microbes and toxicity. While regulations at this time are not stringent, you can still be sued for selling toxic or microbe-ridden plants. Part IV will help you understand your soil, the nutrient requirements for hemp, the fertilizer requirements, and the possible microbes that can cause problems in your industrial hemp crop.

PART IV

PLANNING III: LAYING THE GROUNDWORK—SOIL SCIENCE

16-foot-tall hemp

9. SOIL SCIENCE: LEARN WHAT IS IN YOUR GROUND FOR HEALTHY HEMP

Tobacco has very specific requirements for growing that are very different from hemp. Both require completely different fertilizers, growing atmospheres, soil, temperatures, watering practices, bug prevention, early growth care, humidity, growing enhancement practices, drying, and processing. In essence, they are both completely different plants. Without knowing the differences between the two will lead to failure of the hemp plant, having to burn the plant because of it going hot, or simply being unable to sell it after growth. The knowledge of how to succeed will improve your ability to grow hemp, but it involves throwing out what you think are similar between hemp and tobacco. We will cover all aspects of growing hemp and let you know what the differences between it and tobacco are. In addition, you will see that this chapter supports our earlier statement that if you were thinking of growing hemp in an old tobacco field, you are better off choosing another plot. The other option is to follow our suggestions to get your land and soil ready for hemp. We will explain what growing tobacco will do to your soil, the toxic elements that are left behind as a result of growing tobacco and the typical fertilizers used, and some fixes that will help you obtain soil that is suitable for hemp and grow a safe product.

Tobacco, Fertilizers, and Its Toxic and Depleting Effect on Your Soil

Tobacco can grow in sandy loam soil, but to get maximum growth many use high phosphorus fertilizers and more rarely NPK, nitrogen, phosphorus, and potassium fertilizers. Tobacco can also grow well in standard tomato fertilizer, which makes sense. Tomato is another plant that thrives in sandy loam. For tobacco leaves to weigh more at the dry weight and taste better through the nitrogen reduction, triple superphosphate is applied. Tobacco will not grow as full in natural sandy soil. Hence, the practice started. Most sandy clay soils lack available important nutrients to help plants grow to maximum. This leads to stunted plants when grown in clay unless high topsoil and extra fertilizer and micronutrients are applied.

Tobacco depletes one-third of the total nutrients every growing season. It requires new fertilizer for each season to renew the nutrients in the ground. Tobacco requires the most nitrogen of any plant in the world, so it requires fertilizers that can produce the most to keep crops growing even when the soil is depleted of fertility. Long-term tobacco-grown soils will be completely depleted of nitrogen, potassium, calcium, and phosphorus, all of which are very important in growing hemp, but in completely different levels.

High phosphorus fertilizers like triple phosphate, however, have horrible health effects. Triple and superphosphate contain radioactive elements that can intoxicate plants through roots and elements rising through the soil and getting stuck on trichomes. Phosphorus fertilizers contain radioactive elements such as radioactive lead, polonium, uranium, and radon. All radioactive elements end up inside and outside the tobacco plant. Even Philip Morris reported radioactive elements from fertilizers have a 40% retention inside the actual tobacco leaf and are unable to be eradicated. These radioactive elements then go into the cigarettes and make a pack of cigarettes have a radioactive effect equivalent to 300 x-ray scans on the body. Radon seeps out of the fertilizers originating from the broken up phosphorus rocks and gets absorbed by the tobacco leaves which are like umbrellas over the soil. The tobacco plant also quickly absorbs the radioactive elements into the stalk which then goes throughout the plant. Another method that tobacco gets its radioactivity is the fertilizer attaching to the sticky trichomes of the tobacco leaf and absorb the radioactive elements into the plant itself. It is reported that the polonium and radioactive lead in tobacco lead to 4 cancer-related deaths in every 10,000 deaths per year alone compared to the other 69 carcinogens in tobacco.

Both radioactive lead and polonium are elements that do not leave the body when absorbed. They build up and attack arteries, lungs, kidneys, and the throat. As alpha radiation, they are harmless outside the body, but they can be damaging inside and can build up over time with repeated exposure. The body absorbs these elements through smoking cigarettes. When radioactive lead and polonium are burned, they turn into carcinogens in the smoke. Usually, if the body is exposed to these elements sparsely they would leave over time. However, with repeated exposure, as one would in smoking two packs of cigarettes per day, they remain in the body. In other words, the radioactive elements are not absorbed through secondhand smoke. Instead, they will leave your body through your urine. However, through smoking tobacco, the repeated exposure and absorption of the radioactive elements over time will create a buildup that does not get excreted, which could lead to cancer.

NPK fertilizers for tobacco do not contain these radioactive elements in harmful numbers. There is a natural amount of radioactive elements in the ground already, coming from phosphorus rocks breaking apart in the ground. However, these amounts are usually very small and not harmful. NPK has been found by research and comparison of different soils to have the same sort of small levels of radioactive elements that make it mostly harmless. For this reason, it's the healthier alternative to use, but because of its expense, it is not widely used, especially due to the fact that the tobacco companies drive down the amount offered for tobacco crops, making the use of better fertilizers much less likely.

Hemp, however, will not grow in clay soil, as earlier chapters in this book have established. Fiber varieties were grown with standard fertilizer in sandy soil, and the outcome was an average plant height of 3 to 4-foot plants that could have reached a maximum height of 16 feet tall. Many of the fields in which the plants were grown were former tobacco fields and depleted of nutrients, and a standard fertilizer was not sufficient, as we found out in our conversations with some of the growers from Virginia's research pilot programs.

Using phosphorus fertilizer will not improve growth on hemp. Tobacco sucks up the most nitrogen out of any plant, and when tobacco is grown in a certain soil for several seasons will leave a field with few useful nutrients and fertility for the hemp plant. This will lead to hemp plants that will be stunted or grow very little in that soil. Using phosphorus fertilizers will overpower hemp because hemp needs very little phosphorus in soil to grow. Instead, high phosphorus content will burn the hemp plant because high phosphorus fertilizer will raise the pH level above the 7.0 minimum that hemp needs. 6.5 pH is ideal for hemp. The phosphorus will bring the pH well above that rate and kill the plant. The high levels of phosphorus burns the roots. You will find your hemp plants dead within weeks and very poor growth in phosphorus soil. Hemp needs phosphorus in small, sparse amounts per square centimeter compared to nitrogen, but hemp can be burnt by any nutrient in high amounts. Hemp planted in phosphorus soil can be grown if there are specifically added micronutrients. This type of hemp could be dangerous to sell however due to the risk of high phosphorus fertilizer.

Having high phosphorus soil can come from leftover tobacco fields, over-fertilized fields with manure, or former mining areas. When it's untreated and left alone, the phosphorus will stay in the soil. Think of the soil as salt and hemp as the snail; the combination will kill the snail.

If you have soil that has been fertilized with super phosphate and triple phosphate or has high phosphate presence you will have to dig it up about 3 feet down and should be redone with compost. In high phosphorus soil without fertilizer, you will need to counter with the needed micronutrients so the plant can survive. The simplest way to make your soil habitable for hemp is to dig up the phosphorus soil and cart in enough dark brown compost with a dump truck. You will need to add in necessary micronutrients to your new soil to help your crop grow to its full potential.

Hemp can become toxic in a tobacco field that has undergone years of applications of high phosphate fertilizer. It absorbs all heavy metals through its roots in the soil and distributes it to the buds, which also can catch Lead210 and Polonium210 with the sticky trichomes. Your hemp will then have the same carcinogens as the tobacco: lead, uranium, and polonium. When hemp is smoked, it can lead to the same dangers as with tobacco, cancer and DNA damage from radioactive damage.

To adapt hemp to naturally high phosphorus soil, you will need to add in zinc and iron. It can be applied to the hemp leaves in a water spray of 1% foliar zinc and iron every week to 4 weeks. You must make sure not to spray too often as too much moisture will create mold on the plant and make it more susceptible to bug attacks. Under this method, you will have to use non-phosphorus-containing fertilizer or an N-(Zero)-K fertilizer. Another method to counter high phosphorus is to apply iron and zinc micronutrients into the soil before planting the hemp. This can be the more expensive way of doing it, but it will save you in time of having to go out and spray the plants. You should also avoid adding manure to your field as this will increase phosphorus.

It is also necessary to lime your field to bring it to a better pH. The ideal pH level for hemp is between 6.5 and 7.0, and it is likely that highly phosphorus soil is going to have higher pH.

While phosphorus itself is necessary for hemp growth, excessive phosphorus will have a negative impact. Phosphorus is important for strong root growth, more grain output, and stronger stalks. Because it isn't found in high amounts in normal soil, it is hard for plants to obtain and absorb. When applied to the soil in average amounts, phosphorus is necessary and beneficial to hemp for a better crop. We suggest phosphorus that is based on organic material because of the radioactivity comes from the chemical digestion of rocks. Phosphorus from organic material does not go through the radon break up, while chemical phosphate sources such as triple phosphate fertilizers do. Organic sources include manure and bone meal. Combination fertilizers, N-P-K and ammonium phosphate, should have chemical phosphate in safe amounts for your crop.

However, when you grow tobacco, your phosphorus levels will most likely be too high. We recommend bringing down phosphorus levels before planting hemp. This will improve the environment for your plants before you sink them into the ground, which is better for your plants. You will need to test your planned growing area before planting to make sure your phosphorus levels are at the correct amount.

A longer approach to fix your phosphorus soil is to use high phosphorus absorbing plants such as oilseed plants, but this is a long-term plan that could take several growing seasons and up to 10 years to bring down your natural phosphorus levels down. You will have to dispose of the plants away from the growing area so they don't reabsorb into the ground. Oilseed plants will absorb the nitrogen and other important nutrients that will need to be reintroduced into the soil. By the time you meet the safe phosphorus levels, you could be very low on nitrogen and micronutrients.

An approach that will produce faster results is to grow out a couple of seasons of throwaway hemp. That's right, burn it because it will be a poor plant that you would most likely have trouble selling and will most likely be toxic. You will have to burn the hemp you grow away from your planned hemp growing site so you don't reintroduce the phosphorus and the toxins from tobacco back into the ground. The hemp will purify your soil at a fast rate and take out any heavy metals as well in preparations for your selling crop. Think of the hemp you grow as a practice run. It doesn't have to be perfect, it only has to survive and purify the soil. It shouldn't be worrisome whether or not they are 10 feet tall. They can be lower growth. You can grow the cheapest stuff you can find. The whole plant will suck up the radioactivity from the high phosphorus into the seeds, buds, stalk, and leaves, hence needing to burn each purifying crop away from your growing area. The crop of hemp grown would not be good for breeding either. Because many hemp plants are first generation strains, each plant will be inconsistent. The radioactivity will interfere with the possible outcomes of the hemp plant overall making inconsistent results. Many of the seeds absorbing the radioactive elements are likely to be infertile and not fit for consumption either.

Pesticides should not be used either. Pesticides are known for absorbing in the surrounding ground and you risk adding further toxicity the ground by applying it to your purifying hemp crop. In addition, many states already prohibit their use on hemp. You should use natural and organic bug repellants to keep your plant bug free throughout its life.

You will be using a lot of nitrogen in a short time as well. You should take into consideration that you will use up nutrients very quickly and rotate crop around to bring nonphosphorus nutrients back into the soil. This can be an expensive method; several acres could run up to $10,000.

Cow manure should be avoided when growing hemp. Cow manure is commonly used in many crops as fertilizer. However, cow manure has too much salt to be suitable for hemp. You will end up burning the roots of any hemp plant you put into it and see it die very quickly. You will need to use well-dried, composted chicken manure or rabbit manure on your soil instead because of its lower salt content and high nutrients. You need to pay very close attention to what your fertilizer is made with and not use any that contain wet chicken manure or cow manure. We suggest that you dig out salty cow manure from your growing field if you have already applied cow manure or have in a recent growing season of up to a year and a half. The salt will burn the hemp, and any early growth planted in it is at risk. Cow manure is very easy to obtain and cheap to buy but saving money will not save your crop. Composted or well-dried chicken manure could be harder to find, but you will need it to grow a successful crop.

Hemp is also a soil sponge. It can absorb not only nutrients but also radioactive material from the ground. It can absorb toxic waste much more than any plant on earth as far as it's known. It is so effective at pulling toxicity from the ground, hemp has been planted around the Chernobyl disaster to clean up the nuclear remnants. Now understand when hemp is grown in toxic fertilizer like triple phosphate and superphosphate fertilizers it will absorb a higher amount of toxicities than tobacco. Hemp also has sticky trichomes on its smokable buds, which means the radioactive elements of the fertilizer can stick on and absorb into the bud and become toxic and radioactive, much like tobacco, which is bad news for edibles and smokables. Hemp will absorb radioactivity in its stalk, where you get fiber. This will not help you sell future crops if hemp gains a reputation of toxicity, especially since a lot of the people we know look to hemp as a tobacco substitute because they perceive it as the healthier option.

Make sure to test your soil and fertilizer for the radioactive amount before planting your hemp in it. We spoke with many buyers who will not buy hemp unless you have pre-planting soil tests. As processors, we will not accept your hemp without it. To sell your hemp, it will be important to test your soil and fertilizer for microbials, radioactivity, and pesticides before you start growing. It is a high expense, up to $300 for each test, but highly suggested due to the risks of not knowing what your soil is like ahead of time, and is worthwhile to get your soil to have the proper amounts of nutrition for your hemp to prosper. You have to pay attention if your field had previously grown tobacco. Hemp will also absorb all nicotine in the ground because of its sponge-like qualities as a soil cleaner. If tobacco was grown on your field you shouldn't grow hemp in that field or anywhere there could have been run-off from that field. It may be necessary to see if your field has been deposited with radon from phosphorus fertilizer and nicotine in the ground from disintegrated tobacco leaves left behind. It's a common practice to allow tobacco leaves to collect on the ground after harvest, which allows nicotine to reabsorb into the soil, which will always increase the nicotine of any crop you grow. It was found that spices grown in tobacco fields contain nicotine. Nicotine will cause a toxic hemp plant, and make it unsellable in dealer and processors' eyes. It is necessary to test your soil before planting and either do the work to improve your soil or find the right area for you to grow your hemp to have a sellable product.

Hemp trichomes

There are many laws protecting tobacco growers from a lawsuit if someone gets sick or dies while smoking tobacco. *Hemp growers are not afforded the same lawful protections! You, the grower, can still get sued for producing an unsafe, consumable product!* If someone gets sick or dies from the toxicity of your plant you can get sued for damages and also get sued by the distributor you sold the plant to. You have no laws protecting you from a person dying from smoking your buds or digesting your plant material. It takes lab tests and careful attention to what you are using to grow your plants and what soil you are growing your hemp in. Cannabis itself is seen as not dangerous in comparison to tobacco, so it is expected that no one will die or get harmed when consuming your product. It is your responsibility as the grower to make sure you are making a safe product. When federal regulations come down the line in 2020, guidelines for growing may become quite strict—as they should, since hemp is touted as the healthy alternative for pain relief, anxiety, a healthier alternative for tobacco, and many other health applications. It is better to prepare and instill quality control practices from the start and make your product safe and grow a healthy plant that will be healthy for consumers to ingest or inhale.

Thus, without planting purifying plants to absorb the nicotine, it will stay in the soil for many years. Even if tobacco was grown in the soil 20 years prior, the nicotine will still be in the ground as well as the chemical high phosphorus fertilizer. When tobacco leaves are cut off and left to decompose into the soil the nicotine goes into the ground. Nicotine will not leave the soil if not brought out and if you have had chemical high phosphorus fertilizer in the ground to enhance the tobacco growth you will have radon coming out the ground. The presence of nicotine in your hemp plants can lead to the same cancerous issues that tobacco goes through. Your hemp crop will be tainted with an addictive substance, leading it to be less desirable to buyers along with the legal issues it could bring up with having an outside dangerous element in your crop.

If you live in the south, even if tobacco has not been grown in your soil for years, you will still have to test your ground to ensure that your fields will be a suitable growing environment for growing hemp and go through the effort of appropriately preparing your ground. Tobacco presents special challenges that farmers must overcome. The conditions tobacco and its fertilizers create, as well as the toxic elements they leave behind, are especially harmful for sponge-like hemp. Tobacco-grown soil will have much less available nutrients for hemp to grow than virgin soil. Tobacco takes over <u>one-third</u> of the total needed nutrients from the ground every growing season. If tobacco is grown in that field for years, you will have soil barren of nutrients that have no habitability for new crops. Hemp requires a lot of nutrients to grow for a season. Without those nutrients you will get a very small weak plant that won't produce a lot of buds or seeds. Hemp is the only plant that rivals tobacco for its ability to withdraw nutrients from the soil, so you will have to expect that your soil is lacking even if it has been a number of years since your soil produced tobacco. You will need to replenish the soil and make sure there aren't remnant containments in the soil from the tobacco. The long term growth means many plants of tobacco were reintroduced into the ground when left on the soil. You should dig up the soil and replenish it with dark brown compost or find a different field that is level and has more nutrients in the soil.

Growing in Clay Soil

A lot of the south is made up of clay soil, particularly Virginia, North Carolina, Georgia, parts of eastern Tennessee and South Carolina. Clay soil is not ideal for growing hemp. The growth of hemp will be poor in these soils, and our best suggestion is to grow in pots in greenhouses to maximize growth. The other option is digging out the clay soil 3 feet down across your whole growing field and filling it back in with dark brown compost and a combination of ideal fertilizers to enhance growth. The clay easily saturates and water pools on top of the soil, which will either soak the plant or drown it. If the hemp plant saturates with water, white powder mold will overcome your plants. The clay will also limit root expansion and depth. It is harder for the roots to spread in clay and makes it harder for them to grow stronger because it is more compact and dense than rich, dark topsoil. Clay has small pores, making it more solid and harder for plants to move through it.

Soil consistency is critical. If the soil is too coarse it will hold excess water and choke off much-needed oxygen. Soil that is too fine will not retain enough water or nutrients nor will it provide much of an anchor for the roots from runoff. Rough soil in its natural state is incapable of growing hemp and softening with compost and gypsum is needed. Clay is an example of rough/coarse soil. It will be difficult to produce a profitable yield. Your hemp will likely become overwatered, leading to root rot and wilted dead plants. Silted Sand is a good example of very fine soil, a type that will provide problems with nutrients your hemp plant. Without enough nutrients, your hemp plant will stunt and can be a danger to its health as most sand soil is in hot temperatures that can drought stress.

Studies done by those such as <u>Virginia Agriculture Department</u> show that hemp can grow in clay soil within the humid conditions in the state; however, it will not grow large and full. When combined with depleted tobacco fields, the study produced small hemp with weak stalks and roots, white mold, and toxicity from nicotine and radioactive chemicals rom phosphorus disintegration.

Also, salt left behind from <u>cow manure</u> will not wash away easily in clay soils, which will burn your hemp plants. The lack of drainage contributes to the clay's <u>alkalinity</u> and its ability to harbor toxicity for long periods of time. Thus, if you have clay soil, it will take intervention to create the correct growing conditions for industrial hemp.

To fix clay soils' alkalinity and poor drainage, apply <u>gypsum</u> several months before planting your hemp crop. The best way to keep hard metal chemicals out of your plant is to use non-chemical rock gypsum on your ground. You need to make sure to apply the gypsum several months before planting to break up the hardness of the clay. The gypsum needs time with weathering to open up the clay and make it more habitable for hemp. You will need to get your field bare to the ground, till 2 feet in the clay, and apply what will look like a layer of snow across your soil. Next, till the gypsum into the ground, and let it sit for several months. We suggest applying gypsum one year prior to planting and then again three months before the growing season begins. We suggest you do not apply gypsum after you have planted your hemp. Applying gypsum during your growing season will lead to a change in pH and the plants' nutrient uptake, which could affect its maximum growth and interfere with soil absorption of the gypsum and not improve soil drainage. While this is necessary for general for growing in clay soil, using this method won't improve soil that has a high concentration of salt or phosphorus, so a soil reset is suggested.

It is also suggested that you <u>do not add sand</u> to increase the fertility to your clay soil. While naturally fertile soil has a <u>combination of clay, silt, and sand</u>, adding sand to clay soil will harden the soil, making it more difficult for any plant life to prosper. This is because the thin pores of clay get filled by the little particles of sand, much like the process of making <u>concrete</u>.

Any added manure needs to soak into the ground 2 months before planting your hemp crop. The manure used should be well dried or composted so it does not burn the hemp plant. If the manure is new and wet your seedlings or young plants won't survive, plus fill any surviving plants with dangerous microbials, which we will explain in the next chapter. To help with clay soils you can mix the manure with the gypsum and till it into the clay. The manure will help create pockets in the clay as you let it sit and make it more fertile for hemp growth.

There are other ways sandy soil can be less than ideal for hemp. From our experience sandy soil makes pleasant habitats for bugs and cutworms where they can move around freely.

Natural, untilled sand soil can lose nutrients applied to it due to its lack of absorption. The dryness of the soil might be a benefit to hemp, but the runoff of water will leach the nutrients you try and put back into the ground. Fertilizer won't absorb into to sand soils because sand soils are much finer than loam. Water will wash the nutrients out and down past the root system of the hemp plants, which is not very productive for your seedlings. Plants don't have a chance of using the nutrients in sandy soil. The runoff swiftly sweeps away the nutrients.

If hemp plants had a choice between clay and sandy soil, it would most likely choose sandy soil. The upside to sandy soil is that it's light to work with and warms much more quickly in the spring. The more loam or silt that is present, the more your crop would benefit. Hemp will also have a much easier time developing large root systems in sandy soil because of its "loose" nature.

The Problem of Growing Hemp After Hay, Corn, and Tobacco

You should avoid fields that have grown corn, hay, and/or tobacco. Some corn and all tobacco fields are going to have remnants of pesticides that hemp will drink up. The fields from many growths of corn or tobacco are going to be weak soils which will lead to more bug attacks on your hemp crop. Weaker soils will have crop attacking bugs leftover from the previous crops, and it is known that if a crop is grown in a certain place for several seasons, bugs become more and more of an issue. Tobacco and cornfields also will be low on nutrients which will lead to less growth in hemp and more fertilizer to be needed. Hayfields contain many different bugs and many pests are attracted to the smell of hemp and are more than happy to chew on leaves, stalks, or make homes of the buds. In a hayfield, microbial growth in the soil is going to be higher, meaning growing toxic hemp plants that you can't sell. Hayfields will have less concentration in controlling microbial growth and what bugs are in the plants. Hay that is cut down and is made wet by the rain than on the ground becomes fields for microbial growth, which stays on the ground even after the hay is collected. Microbial growth is an issue with leftover tobacco leaves and corn products left on the ground to reabsorb into the soil. Pesticides and herbicides absorb into corn and tobacco, and when left on the ground, reabsorbed into the soil. Hemp will reabsorb back up the contaminants and deliver into its leaves and buds during growing, making a toxic plant.

Cornfields prosper in <u>low-nitrogen</u> soil, helping the plant to become resilient. Hemp is the opposite of this case. Hemp needs a lot of nitrogen. Nitrogen is one of the most important ingredients in hemp growing. Growing hemp in a cornfield will lead to small stunted plants with low bud growth. Remember that hemp is a soil-sucker, meaning it needs lots of nutrients. Corn can thrive in low-nutrient soils, creating incompatible growing conditions with growing hemp. Cornfields are also going to have a high amount of insecticide in the ground, which hemp will fully absorb.

To handle a low nitrogen field, compost it. You will need more organic material in the ground to ensure growth and reintroduce nitrogen. Laying it on the surface will be ineffective: you will need to dig 3 feet into the ground and refill it with compost so the roots of hemp can move and absorb nutrients around it.

The second option for nitrogen-filled hemp growth is a rich soil pit. A rich soil pit is an equivalent of digging out a 3 foot wide by a 3-foot tall container in the ground and filling it with nutritious compost and fertilizer. This can be difficult with clay soil, as the clay will trap water from leaving the organic pit, essentially creating a clay pot that holds the water in. If this happens, the roots will rot with mold and be susceptible to toxic microbials. The clay will have to be tilled with gypsum first as deep as you can go to help soil drainage. The clay should be tilled with gypsum about 3 times over a year before growing to help drainage. Another way to help drainage is to pre-dig the holes the year prior and apply heavy covers of gypsum inside the holes. This method should be used 3 times with the last time coming about 3 months to a month before planting.

You will need to watch out for swampy soil. Swampy soil is soil that saturates fully and is wet to touch. Tennessee has constant issues with <u>swampy soil</u> and loses a lot of their crops because of it.

To get help to get rid of surface insecticide and herbicides from the soil you will need a waste crop to empty the soil of it. It may not empty all of it, and not in areas where it seeped deeply in the soil. If the herbicides and insecticides are deeply in the soil, it's best to avoid that field altogether because the roots will absorb it. There's little you can do to the soil if it's seeped 2 to 3 feet into the ground. You will need to dig a hole the equivalent to the depth of hemp roots, 3-4 feet deep, to test the soil if you find traces of pesticides in the soil. The longer it is in the soil, the deeper in the ground it is going to be from drainage. If it is known that the pesticides were in the soil a long time ago (a year to 2 years beforehand), or consistently used on previous crops such as corn or tobacco, or used long term on that field, that soil should not be used at all. It's better to assume the insecticide is already root-deep. If it is surface level, it is possible to draw it back out with either mint or sunflowers. The crop should be planted for about 6 growing seasons and then tested again. However, <u>sunflowers</u> can bring in pests that can affect hemp. However, sunflowers tend to mop up your field deeper into the ground, whereas mint will mop up the surface. Yet, mint is known for drawing up nicotine from the ground.

Mint

You will have to safely dispose of the waste crop. If you let the plants sit in the soil after cutting down, the pesticides and toxins will reabsorb into the soil. The crop should be burned after each growing season away from your planting soil. You will need a safe dump site away from water runoff so other soil sites do not get contaminated in case those sites are going to grow hemp for you as well. Our suggestion is a large metal garbage container or dump truck bucket, where you can do your large-scale burning and store of the ashes.

Get Rid of the Fake Corn Too

You will need to immediately till the ground of a field and kill any Johnsongrass that near or on your growing site. Johnsongrass, an invasive species that grows what looks like tiny ears of corn, is known to attract

Johnson Grass

harmful bugs, such as aphids, which can bring just about every disease or issue hemp can have. Not only is Johnsongrass an issue with bugs, but it is also because when stressed by drought, herbicide, or frost can produce enough cyanide to kill a cattle— great protection for the survival of the species but devastating to farmers.

A common complaint from the cannabis industry is that Johnsongrass will quickly grow larger than your hemp plant and strangle any sun that it will get. If you see one of these in your hemp field, pull it out quickly. They can already be in your soil for up to 15 years and can pop up to quickly to overtake your hemp crop to kill it with hemp-attacking bugs and snuffing out the light from your hemp crop. It is commonly found all over the south and common in hayfields because of its tendency to take over areas.

Many processors and hemp retailers are neat freaks. You have to look at growing hemp as growing a food crop, not a fiber crop. From our many experiences in talking to other processors and retail dispensaries, many dispensaries required full lab reports showing proof that pesticides weren't used, that it didn't test positive for radioactive materials, there were no microbials, and that the THC came under the legal limit of 0.3 delta-9 THC. They also required pre-growing soil tests to make sure there were no contaminants in the soil beforehand. While some don't have as strict of buying regulations, would you trust someone trying to sell you untested hemp at this point? Many CBD oil samples have already tested positive with containing pesticides and heavy metals. What those manufacturers do is buy up as many tons of hemp as they can as cheap as they can, and believe that they boil out when cooking the oil. This is not true, as the news agencies are finding out, and they love to capitalize on stories about how hemp contains harmful substances when people think they are consuming a healthier alternative. When the FDA does come down with the hammer, farmers will experience severe consequences. Currently, based on statements from the FDA, they will not approve CBD oil processing unless you have a top-of-the - line manufacturing center with all approved items. This conveys that the scrutiny has already begun, and the public and Congress are eager for regulations. As soon as the FDA can research CBD, its potential, and the potential problems, the regulations will come.

Thus, it is best to establish your hemp farm so that the hemp can prosper and you can generate healthy hemp from the start. Especially for ingestible, smokable products, we suggest you invest the money in a greenhouse, not only to protect your investments, but also to protect you from future lawsuits. If you establish good practices from the start and grow in good soil, minimizing the chances for toxic, sickly plants, you increase your chances of success. You will not be disappointed for low offerings for your hemp because it is stunted, fungus, and bug-ridden. You will be able to prove that you are growing a great, healthy product through proper soil preparation, providing the labs to prove that you are a person who the purchasers can trust, and enjoy profits in this industry right from the start. All it takes is a bit of capital, elbow grease, and the ability to acknowledge the reality right in front of you.

Now you have chosen your crop and gotten your plan together to ensure your soil is safe and nutritious for hemp plants. You learned how to adjust your soil conditions. Next we will discuss microbials, the other issue that could sink your crop like a lead zeppelin.

10. MICROBIALS: YOUR UNSEEN ENEMIES

You are probably wondering why you should care about microbials. Even though microbials are commonly found in tobacco, it seems that people do not worry about it. We can only surmise that the reason for this neglect on this subject is because of the well-known carcinogenic nature of cigarettes, despite the plethora of information available on the subject. Even e-cigarettes often contain fungi and toxins. Tobacco companies know about it also: one of their own employees wrote a 37-page paper regarding the subject.

You might be wondering, is it possible that I can sell a toxic plant when I believe I am supplying the public with a safe miracle drug? Yes, you can. All these infections are possible in hemp and have already occurred. Just recently at the end of 2018, Michigan Cannabis tested positive for having E.coli and salmonella. Strains Citrix, Gelato, Green Crack, and Oreoz were also found.

Hemp differs from tobacco. While it can be smoked like tobacco, it needs to be treated as food because much of it winds up in food products, unlike tobacco. For this reason, it's more like a temperamental food product. It needs a strong pre-program before growing to ensure it is a medicinal and healing product like it has always meant to be. Testing is paramount to finding what is in your plant, whether disease or making sure you got what was advertised. Testing periodically throughout the season and taking care of your crop will prevent these negative and unwanted issues from showing up. For industrial hemp, it is not as simple as throwing it in the ground and making a million dollars as people want you to believe.

We've been talking about microbials and mycotoxins the whole book and telling you issues they can bring. Because of this, as a grower, you want to be above that to avoid sickening your family, friends, and the general public with the hemp you grow. You will be producing an unsafe product through neglectful farming practices, which can lead to lawsuits. It's much easier and proactive to prevent a microbial problem rather than lose everything you have because you didn't take the time to stay on top of any issues that can arise with your crop. It's important to test your crop after drying to ensure the safety of your crop and those who buy it, but you will be above the rest being able to prevent your soil from having microbials before growing. From a marketing and sales point of view, demonstrating that your product is safe beyond a shadow of a doubt is not only proactive, but a smart business strategy to build trust between yourself and your buyers and consumers. It sets your product above all of the rest. Now it's time to go into detail. To understand the issues they can bring into your crop, you have to understand what they are and where they come from.

Ants and Aphids: What Causes Microbials?

Before we go into an extensive amount of detail about microbials, first let's discuss what brings them to your crop. One of the main causes of microbials is aphids. They go hand in hand with ants and wet, saturated soil. Their chew marks leave the inside of the plant exposed and fighting infections from fungi and bacteria. Their honeydew excretions that come from eating the plant attract fungi which will turn your hemp plant toxic. The honeydew is the effect that causes microbial toxicities. If you have ants on your plants, you have aphids.

Aphid

Aphid infestation can be indicators of various infections such as powdery mildew, caused by their physical, digestive, and fecal secretions on a plant, which is called honeydew. Aphids carry viruses in their mouths and secretions, which are left in the honeydew on the plants.

Types of Microbials

Microbials refer to two sets of toxins: mycotoxins and endotoxins. Simply put, mycotoxins are dangerous fungi and endotoxins refer to viruses such as E. coli and salmonella. Many mycotoxins are things we want to prevent and test for before growing. Endotoxins are things we can prevent through cleanliness. In the cannabis industry, you will hear microbials more than any other. The term microbial is used mostly in the cannabis industry even though the issues it refers to affects all plants and is a concern of any food crop.

Specifically, <u>microbials</u> refers to microorganisms such as bacteria, pathogens, yeast, E.coli, Aspergillus, Fusarium, and Botrytis. These organisms create adverse health effects when they come in contact with the inside of our bodies and can be deadly. According to <u>Willow Industries</u>: "Like any agricultural product, cannabis is susceptible to microorganisms that could potentially harm consumers. In fact, in 2017, approximately 15% of all commercially grown flower had microbial contamination. By 2020, this is projected to be a $3 billion problem."

Microbials are a complete cannabis industry issue. Fiber infected in certain mildews can create a fiber structure that will get workers sick when in contact with microbials on a daily basis. Products such as fiberboard made from hemp fiber that has been infected with mold can create a building with dangerous mold.

Grain that is infected with mold and E.coli is <u>dangerous to consumers</u> when ingested. The edible seeds, even when crushed into oil, can become harmful with microbial infections. The process of <u>cooking the oil</u> won't cook out microbials which can live after being heated or boiled. A lot of times CBD oil contains hemp oil, and it has been reported that <u>CBD oil</u> brands do test positive with dangerous levels of microbials.

We have spoken with many CBD oil companies who spread a myth: they believe that microbials get cooked out in the process. However, lab tests prove this belief as a myth and nothing more. The following sections will provide you with what you need to know about microbials so you can arm yourself with the knowledge you will need in order to produce a safe product.

Mycotoxins

Mycotoxins are poisonous substances produced by <u>fungi</u>, a group of organisms that contains molds, yeasts, and mushrooms. Mycotoxins are the spores of fungi and mold that are harmful and even <u>lethal</u> to human and animal health is very low amounts of exposure. Mycotoxins are listed as <u>the most important chronic dietary risk factor</u> for human health, higher than synthetic contaminants, plant toxins, food additives, and pesticide residues. Most mycotoxins are <u>carcinogenic</u> and cause liver cancer or illnesses in either large doses at once or exposure over time. Mycotoxins are as small as 0.1 microns per spore. As a point of comparison, <u>human hair</u> is approximately 1000 times thicker. One guarantee is you have mycotoxins if you have mold or fungi in your crop.

Damaged hemp plant

The term mycotoxin was coined in 1962 in the aftermath of an unusual veterinary crisis near London, England, during which approximately 100,000 turkeys died. When this mysterious turkey X disease was linked to a peanut meal contaminated with mold spores from Aspergillus flavus (aflatoxins), the event sensitized scientists to the possibility that other mold by-products might be deadly. Mycotoxins are characterized by being toxic in low concentrations.

Mycotoxin Diseases

Mycotoxins can cause a set of diseases known as mycotoxicoses and be deadly to an immune system compromised individuals. The majority of mycotoxicoses come from the consumption of infected foods. Infection is possible through ingestion, skin contact, and inhalation where it will enter the bloodstream via the lungs. They can inhibit protein synthesis, damage certain white blood cells, inhibit particle clearance of the lung, and increase sensitivity to the bacterial endotoxin E. coli.

Mycotoxicoses can be either acute or chronic. Acute toxicity has an immediate toxic reaction, while chronic toxicity is low-dose exposure over a long time, resulting in cancers and other generally damaging diseases. The biggest burden of mycotoxicoses is chronic illnesses: cancers, kidney toxicity, and immune system damage.

In common terms smoking or digesting mycotoxin-infected hemp will cause ill health effects, especially over time. If someone is taking CBD oil made from your plant and it was infected they will get sick taking it over time or have an immediate mycotoxicoses reaction. One of the mycotoxins' favorite spots to settle in is the lungs, it makes an ample breeding ground for molds and it can eventually develop either mold balls or Aspergillus growths. Mold balls attached to the lungs need to be surgically removed.

Some mycotoxin molds are more toxic when ingested. Cannabis edibles can become toxic when myotoxins are included in the products. Making, let's say, gummies from mycotoxic hemp will lead to mycotoxicoses. Things such as headaches and nausea are mild effects from having it, while diarrhea and more severe consequences can result from long term repeated exposure to that infected brand of gummies. The World Health Organization explained the toxicity of mycotoxins:

> The maximum levels for mycotoxins in food are very low due to their severe toxicity. For example, the maximum levels for aflatoxins set by the Codex in various nuts, grains, dried figs, and milk are in the range of 0.5 to 15 µg/kg (a µg is one-billionth of a kilogram). The Codex maximum limit for patulin in apple juice is 50 µg/L. Exposure to mycotoxins needs to be kept as low as possible to protect the people.

In 2004 in Kenya, 125 people died and nearly 300 others fell ill after eating aflatoxin-contaminated maize. The deaths were mainly associated with homegrown maize that was infected and not properly dried before storage. Due to food shortages, farmers may have been harvesting maize earlier than normal to prevent thefts from their fields, so that the grain had not fully matured and was more susceptible to infection.

In general, mycotoxin exposure is more likely to occur in parts of the world where poor methods of handling and storage as well as where few regulations exist to protect exposed populations. Few regulations exist for mycotoxins in hemp. Without care and neglectful farming practices, mycotoxins are a true threat in this budding industry. If you do not take care in your farming practices from the start, you can not only make people severely ill, but you can bring down the entire industry, and all of your future earnings you can make from hemp will be threatened.

Individuals with compromised immune systems rely on safe and pure cannabis for treatments. Also, when cannabis is smoked, it enters the bloodstream quicker and this can intensify the effects of the contaminants. Even dead organisms may trigger <u>allergies and asthma attacks</u>. Mycotoxic mold, *Aspergillus*, is especially dangerous to immune-compromised individuals with asthma in whom the airborne spores can lead to a debilitating or sometimes fatal invasive infection. Aspergillosis begins when the spores are inhaled through the mouth where the fungus finds ample breeding grounds in the lungs that can quickly lead to a deadly infection. Once the infection starts it can cause serious, and sometimes fatal, bleeding of the lungs. Due to the invasive nature of the infection, aspergillosis can quickly spread to kidneys, heart, and even the brain. <u>Aspergillosis</u> is capable of spreading impressively fast and commonly results in death.

Though rare, there have been documented cases of healthy individuals developing an aspergillosis infection through cannabis as recent as 2016. The danger is acquired through <u>smoking</u> medical cannabis. Even though smoking burns cannabis, it does not reach 200 degrees, which is required to effectively kill *Aspergillus* spores. Those with <u>compromised immune systems</u>, either through disease or medical treatment, are at serious risk of developing an aspergillosis infection if they are using infected hemp to help treat their system

Those at risk of dying to the mycotoxic <u>Aspergillus</u> disease are:
> People who are taking immune system suppressive drugs from taking bone or organ transplants
> People with low white blood cell count from chemotherapy or AIDS.
> People with asthma
> People on long term corticosteroid therapy

Due to the immediate danger of ingesting mycotoxins, the legal level of mycotoxins in various nuts, grains, dried figs, and milk the maximum range from 0.5 to 15 µg/kg. For fumonisins (from Fusarium molds), the maximum levels in grain from raw maize and maize flour and meal are 4000 and 2000 µg/kg, respectively. However there is little federal regulation on mycotoxins. Regulations vary state-by-state.

Types of Mycotoxins

Mycotoxins are present in several different subsets with different levels of toxicity that vary by the type of fungi. The ones that affect hemp plants are aflatoxins, ochratoxins, and Fusariums.

Two closely related species of molds or fungi are mainly responsible for producing the mycotoxins of public health significance: <u>Fusarium and</u>

<u>Aspergillus</u>. They are the most problematic for humans and are commonly found in hemp grown in humid conditions and have been attacked by aphids. Both fungi are a threat to hemp crops. Now you are able to see why we encourage growing in greenhouses under tightly-controlled conditions—at the microlevel.

Fusarium. <u>Fusarium</u> is a fungus that has the potential to wipe out an entire cannabis crop. Once plants are infested, it can cause devastating root rot and wilting that will ensure not a single bud is harvested or smoked. This fungus can wreak absolute havoc on cannabis plants and cannot be treated once detected. This makes prevention of the utmost importance. Fusarium is one of the most difficult problems in the <u>cannabis garden</u> to fix and even more difficult to detect on your own.

Fusarium wilt

Fusarium can <u>lie dormant</u> within the soil for years at a time before it becomes active and detrimentally affect crops. This makes the fungus incredibly hard to detect, meaning many of your plants could be vulnerable to an attack without any warning signs. The dormant cells spring into action when they detect a suitable host plant, with cannabis being an ideal target on their radar. The <u>spores can easily spread</u> through farming tools, water runoff, and other infected weeds around your crop. Since Fusarium dwells and thrives only in soil, growing <u>hydroponically</u> is a good option to avoid it.

Fusarium types cause wilting and root rot, a different type responsible for each. Some of the first signs of the wilting damage caused by a <u>Fusarium attack</u> will manifest in leaves quickly, turning them to shades of yellow and brown and the tips to curl upward. <u>Fusarium root rot</u> will cause the roots to turn red or the stalk to split at the base and then spread to the rest of the plant.

If your crop becomes <u>infested</u>, burn it and start anew in a far-away field. The crop will not be sellable as its yield will make people sick. It can severely affect people with a weakened immune system, which can come back to you if that person dies as a large lawsuit.

Fusarium fungus is attracted to <u>hot and humid conditions</u>, however, <u>clay soil</u> helps prevent Fusarium due to its higher pH content, but it is not an appropriate prevention. Applying clay to sandy soils practically turns the soil into concrete.

Moisture content is higher in immature crops and increases their susceptibility to mold damage. Also, not <u>harvesting</u> in a timely manner can be an invitation to insect or mold invasion.

Before even planting crops, some growers may opt to use natural organic fungicides in an attempt to eliminate the risk of Fusarium. These include preparations of <u>nettle and horsetail</u>. Adding <u>compost tea or bacterial food like molasses</u> can help to support healthy bacteria and fungi within the soil. Some terpenes found in some marijuana strains are anti-fungal and anti-bacterial. <u>Peppermint</u> crops are also another preventive agent against mold and bacteria. We can also use <u>fungicides</u> such as propolis and ponytail or sulfur.

Fusarium is toxic due to the toxin called trichothecenes (tri-ko-fee-seens). Trichothecenes can be acutely toxic to humans, causing rapid irritation to the skin or intestinal mucosa and lead to diarrhea. Trichothecenes are common in wheat and can be found in wheat fields. Another toxin from Fusarium affects cornfields called <u>fumonisins</u>. These toxins can penetrate deep into plants and do not just grow on the surface. Once it is inside, it is a lost plant. <u>Trichothecenes</u> are strongly associated with chronic and fatal toxic effects in animals and humans. Trichothecenes are the longest-lasting mycotoxin. Things like ultraviolet light or freezing temperatures do not have much effect on trichothecene mycotoxins. Trichothecene mycotoxins can be absorbed through the skin as well. It takes fire at 500 degrees Fahrenheit (260 degrees Celsius) for half an hour or fire at 900 degrees Fahrenheit (482 degrees Celsius) for 10 minutes <u>to destroy trichothecene mycotoxins</u>. Fumonisins found in corn have been linked to esophagus cancer, and The International Agency for Research on Cancer has evaluated the cancer risk of fumonisins to humans and classified them as <u>group 2B</u> (most likely carcinogenic). Hemp will absorb these elements up from the ground and the danger Fusarium will affect it as well.

Botrytis:

Botrytis, a. k. a. bud rot or gray mold, shows itself through a thick white dense spider web on the bud. However, leaves and other parts of the hemp can be affected. The buds infected with <u>Botrytis</u> cannot be consumed in any way. Botrytis may cause winegrower's lung, a rare form of hypersensitivity pneumonitis (a respiratory allergic reaction in infected individuals) with repeated exposure to it. While not lethal, it is severe enough where the only way it resolves is a trip to the <u>doctor</u>. Botrytis can remain dormant for long periods on the hemp plant before it <u>activates</u>.

Excessive application of nitrogen will increase the incidence of disease for grey mold while not improving yields. <u>Gray mold</u> thrives in high humidity and reduced light. To help infected crop you can cut off infected material and apply rubbing alcohol to the area around it to purify it. You will need to clean your cutting tool with alcohol as well each time you cut off an infected piece.

Gray mold

Aspergillus. The most concerning fungi is <u>Aspergillus,</u> or powdery mildew. It's one of the "<u>Horsemen of the Apocalypse</u>" for hemp crops. Powdery mildew is easily recognizable by its look of white flour sprinkled all over the leaves. It starts with white spots on the upper side of the leaves and eventually spread to the whole plant. It can infect the stems, buds, and seeds. Any bud produced by an infected plant will have <u>a moldy inferior taste</u>. However, any part of the plant infected by powdery mildew should not be digested at all, not through smoking or eating. Aspergillus is one of the most dangerous toxin-producing fungi with two possible toxins: aflatoxins and ochratoxins. When hemp plants are infected and the buds are infected they should be disposed of, burned, and bleached. The ashes shouldn't be anywhere near your hemp crop, as aflatoxins cannot be burned and can find your way back to your crop through the air. Aspergillus, even by biological standards, can <u>travel great distances in the air</u>. <u>New York State</u> regulations also list "Aspergillus species" as a required item that labs must test for legality.

Aspergillus occurs naturally in almost everything in <u>nature</u>. Aspergillus is most commonly found in the soil around us, where it thrives on organic debris and dead plant material. While Aspergillus predominantly <u>grows underground</u>, its spores grow in number rapidly in the air with each fungus capable of producing thousands of more. These spores are everywhere. We most likely breathe them in anytime we go <u>outside</u>. In natural air-born levels, they aren't dangerous. They become dangerous when they propagate onto a food or smoking product and enter our bodies all at once. Billions of spores can be on a powdery mildew-infected bud or leaf, and that's when it can become fatal.

Powdery mildew

Airborne Aspergillus can enter your greenhouses or drying rooms through an HVAC system, or simply by opening the door to the outside. These spores are commonly spread through strong air currents and are found both indoors and out. We recommend ionizers over HEPA filters and can help steer you in the right direction on what models will be most effective for your purposes.

The best way to protect against powdery mildew is through prevention. This fungus is almost impossible to exterminate 100% if it appears at the end of the flowering period. This fungus can be taken care of when it appears, but that is a long battle that we don't want to go through. Good preparation and growing and drying practices are key to preventing it from showing up. First, you should test for the presence of any fungus or yeast in your soil. If it is, you will have to be vigilant about extra moisture over long periods of time.

Tobacco, wheat, and corn fields suffer from Aspergillus. Growing mint can help prevent fungus growths as well as mixing in natural ingredients in the soil that promote good bacteria like molasses. Next, you will have to buy verified clones or seeds as both can already be pre-infected with the fungus if the plant they came from suffering from it. When planting, plants need to be appropriately separated to allow for air circulation and should be kept away from walls. Preventative measures include not watering plants during humid conditions or at night when dew will cover the plants and applying copper sulfate and propolis with consistency. If you start seeing signs you need to react immediately. You can combine 1 part milk and 9 parts water to put into a spray bottle and liberally coat infected plants. It will need to be reapplied weekly. Sulfur can also be a good fungicide against powdery mildew. To help prevent powdery mildew during growing is to help airflow by trimming the bottom stems. You will need to collect the trimmings from the ground so they do not attract powdery mildew. Sometimes crops become contaminated with powdery mildew because of drought stress, which weakens the plants and increases their susceptibility to insect damage and other attacks.

Aflatoxin. Aflatoxins are a type of mycotoxin produced by Aspergillus species of fungi, The umbrella term aflatoxin refers to four different types of mycotoxins. Certain molds produce aflatoxins and are amongst the most poisonous mycotoxins. Aflatoxins have drawn more attention than other toxins due to the acutely toxic nature and powerful carcinogenic effect their naturally-occurring mycotoxins have on humans and also animals. Aflatoxin B1, the most toxic, is a potent carcinogen and has been directly correlated to adverse health effects, such as liver cancer. The International Agency for Research on Cancer classified aflatoxin B1 as a group I, very dangerous, a carcinogen.

The liver is the organ aflatoxins most often affect. Children appear to be most susceptible when in contact with aflatoxins. Incidence of liver problems (including cancer) has been observed in selected geographic areas where aflatoxin intake was high. Large doses of aflatoxins can lead to acute poisoning and can be life-threatening, usually through liver damage.

You will need to wear protective masks and disposable gloves when handling infected plants. According to an early study in the toxicity of aflatoxins, two previously healthy young adult workers at a Dutch peanut processing plant had contracted respiratory cancer after working with the aflatoxin dust from infected peanuts.

Ochratoxin. Ochratoxin A is produced by several species of Aspergillus of the Aspergillus toxins, the only ochratoxin is potentially as important as the aflatoxins. Ochratoxin A has been labeled as a carcinogen and a kidney damaging toxin, as well as being linked to tumors in the human urinary tract. Studies have indicated that ochratoxin A is a liver toxin and an immune suppressant. It is rated as a human carcinogen by The International Agency for Research on Cancer (category 2B).

Ochratoxin A was discovered in 1965. Shortly thereafter, it was isolated from a commercial corn sample in the United States. It was then recognized as a potent nephrotoxin, a damager of the kidneys. Ochratoxin A can be spread from in barley, oats, rye, wheat, coffee beans to hemp. Barley has a particularly high likelihood of contamination.

Ochratoxin is another toxin found in Aspergillus and mold species found in hemp. It can exist with endotoxins, aflatoxins, Botrytis, and Fusarium toxins all at the same time. This would create a severely toxic plant. The way to prevent this toxin is the same as keeping powdery mildew away.

Endotoxins

At the other end of microbials, you have endotoxins. Endotoxins are bacteria that react negatively inside our bodies. They are different from mycotoxins in that they are not products from molds, but rather originate from feces. Composting eliminates all endotoxins from the common infecting material, fresh cow manure. The term "endotoxin" is occasionally used to refer to any cell bacterial toxin in bacteriology but usually refers to pathogens such as Escherichia coli (E.coli), Salmonella, Shigella, Pseudomonas, Neisseria, Haemophilus influenza (the Flu), Bordetella pertussis and Vibrio cholerae.

Endotoxins are heat stable; in other words, boiling endotoxins for 30 minutes does not change or break down an endotoxin. This is quite different from the belief of CBD manufacturers. Certain powerful agents such as superoxide, peroxide, and hypochlorite, have been reported to neutralize endotoxins.

Food or water tainted with certain strains of E. coli bacteria can leave you fighting for your life, especially if your immune system is compromised or you're very young or very old, and you cannot see it or smell it. E. coli comes from human and animal wastes. E.coli types are dangerous to people in producing severe illness or death through toxins. During rainfall and runoff, E. coli may be washed into creeks, rivers, streams, lakes, or groundwater. When these are used as sources of drinking water—and the water is not treated or inadequately treated—E. coli may end up in drinking water. However, since most cases of E. coli contamination are passed from person to person, good personal hygiene is critical to protecting yourself. If your soil or water is contaminated with E. coli, the bacteria can survive for years. The dangerous species of E.coli Endotoxin, E. coli O157: H7, is quite hardy. It can survive for extended periods in water and soil, under frozen temperatures, and in dry conditions. It also can adapt to acidic conditions of clay soil. The organism is only destroyed by thorough cooking at 160 degrees.

When a hemp plant is infected, E. coli can grow and colonize on the surface of the plant. Researchers have shown that a small number of bacteria can invade inside the plant, where they become protected from washing. The same group has shown that E. coliO157: H7 can colonize the roots of plants. This means that it is possible that endotoxins can enter the soil and affect the roots of your hemp plant and then directly into the hemp plant itself. E. coli can also infect the inside of buds and leaves.

Symptoms characterized by severe abdominal cramping can appear within hours or can also take up to 10 days to show up. Some people may be afflicted with bloody diarrhea or non-bloody diarrhea. Seizures or strokes may occur. Frequently, no fever is present. Some people may show no symptoms at all but can still carry the bacteria and pass it on to people who will become sick. In a small number of cases, E. coli contamination can lead to hemolytic uremic syndrome (HUS), a life-threatening condition that kills three to five percent of people who come down with it. Some people who recover still have to contend with lifelong complications that can include blindness, paralysis, and kidney failure. By selling an E.coli infected hemp plant you risk the death of an individual or permanent bodily damage. If your workers have E.coli, they should not be working or handling your tools. Tools need to be sanitized with bleach after each use and the plants examined. Bleach is an effective killer of E.coli for your tools.

E.coli can also come from contact with byproducts from mammals, reptiles, fowl, insects and unpasteurized animal products. They can also become contaminated through direct or indirect contact with cattle, deer, and sheep. E. coli is most prevalent in cattle in particular both beef and dairy cows. Other known carriers include birds, insects, and squirrels. While the bacteria do not appear to make these animals sick, the animals carry and shed the bacteria in their feces. After turning your compost pile or doing any other manure-related activity, thoroughly wash your hands and any other contaminated body parts with soap and warm water. Wash the tools that had direct contact with the manure. Importantly, don't use the same tools for manure handling that you use for crop harvesting (buckets or gloves, for example). Remove manure-contaminated clothing, including shoes and gloves, before going into the house and especially before eating, drinking or preparing food.

Those infected with flu can infect you crop and cause an outbreak. Workers who have the flu shouldn't be out in the field because of the risk of getting the disease on your plants. A sneeze on a leaf can go overlooked into the public's hands. If this does occur and you can locate the infected plant, you can wash the bud off with a spray solution of soap and water.

In this chapter, we provided you a good primer on your hemp crop's unseen tiny enemies that can infect your plants, people, animals, and threaten your entire crop. As daunting and scary some of these microbials can be, the good news is that the actions you take to establish your hemp in good soil, growing practices that discourage the growth of microbials, and taking on a proactive approach to help your hemp plants even when challenges present themselves can prevent many of these problems from occurring. The good farming practices explained in this book and future books in this series will help you avoid many of these issues so your plants will grow into healthy, strong hemp. Since we have been heavily discussing the importance of lab tests, it helps to know the types of lab tests you will not only need, but want, so you can proudly demonstrate to your potential buyers that you put out a superior product. This is what the next chapter will explain.

11. TESTING FOR HEALTHY PLANTS

When you have ideal soil, hemp becomes more bug-resilient. The nutrients help strengthen the immune system of the plant so it can fight against bug attack rather than wilt and die. That's why it is important to change the soil conditions in your fields to match the ideal grounds for hemp. Each season you will have to check on your nutrient amount after growing hemp to bring it back up to ideal levels to make the hemp grow.

Lab tests can do two things. Not all lab tests will cost a lot or require a test from a laboratory, especially as you prepare your soil to provide the growing environment you need to grow healthy hemp plants. It takes all of the guessing out of your preparations for adding the correct balance of nutrients to the soil. In addition, lab tests can give you an added edge when you sell your product and can even help protect you against false lab results.

Test Your Soil and Water

Now that we've gone through many growing scenarios for hemp we shall look towards testing your soil. The next step before growing and after you've chosen where to grow is making sure your ground is ready for a hemp crop. Testing will tell you what nutrients your ground may have or lack in. Knowing before-hand what is wrong or right in your soil because then you can set your soil right and come up with a perfect crop. You can add in the needed micro and macronutrients that may be missing from the soil through direct deposit with water. You will need to know what you are growing in before starting.

You will need these tests when selling and make your crop worth more if you come out with a great crop. The nutrient amount, pH level, microbial, and pesticide/herbicide are all different tests you have to take and know.

Nutrients tests will come in handy. Many come in kits that test for pH and major macronutrients such as phosphorus, nitrogen, and potassium. Low levels of calcium and magnesium could kill your plants. Sulfur being another overlooked nutrient necessary to growth and also sparse in most soils and fertilizers. Phosphorus tests will help let you know if you have a dangerous amount, or not enough to grow strong roots and a thick stalk. Nitrogen is commonly depleted in soils, especially in fields that have suited other crops. From our professional experience in helping Virginia growers with their hemp crops, nitrogen deficiency for hemp is very common in fields that had previously grown other crops. Virgin soil would be more suitable in nitrogen and other macronutrients but still may need more micronutrients to ensure growth.

One thing you need is to test your planned water resource's pH level. Natural rainwater will usually be from 6.5-6.8 with 6.8 being more ideal for hemp, and it is our preferred water source, since the clay ground contains water that is slightly in the acidic side. Standard pH test strips can be purchased from your local hardware store by the dozens so you can recheck your water often throughout the planting. Water in excess of a 6.8 pH level can kill your hemp plant and make it wilt. Some well water can be high in pH, so attention should be paid no matter what water source you use. Interestingly, we found that our well water right out of the ground is on the acidic side due to the clay soil.

You will also have to test the pH of your soil to ensure your hemp's growth. Appropriate pH levels are vital to the growth of hemp. The maximum acidic level it can take is 7.0, its maximum base a 6.5. If you are out of this range it will wilt and kill your plant and leave behind several other visual issues in your plant. You will have to measure your soil's pH balance after you add nutrients into your soil and throughout the growing season. Adding in too much of one nutrient can affect your soil pH, as well as the pH of the water you are using, will affect the soil pH. You will also want to test in your field throughout your growing period as hemp draws nutrients from the ground. A pH test can help you keep track of what nutrients you will need to replace in your soil as the growing season progresses. You will need to watch what the pH on your fertilizer and topsoil pH is when buying it, and if necessary, test the content to verify it is in fact in the right range for your plant. Another option for your fertilizer is contacting the fertilizer directly for a lab certificate of authenticity of the pH and contents of the fertilizer.

Radon is another important test for your water system or water source, especially if you live on an old tobacco farm or you have grown tobacco in your fields. Radon can be found in wells and even natural water systems. As you remember, hemp is a soil sucker that can take radioactive material out of the soil. By watering hemp with radon-infected water, the roots would absorb the radon and increase the radioactivity in your plants.

Radium, Lead 210, and Polonium 210 are radioactive tests you will have to do for your soil if you have grown tobacco on that field with Triple superphosphate fertilizer or any nearby field. There are natural levels of these elements in the soil at all times, but the concern comes in when chemical phosphorous breaks down in large concentrations. The worldwide standard is usually close to or around <u>370 Bq/kg</u> on radioactive substances found in public products. Anything over this is considered dangerous. The EPA defines Bq/kg as radioactive nucleus decays per second per kilogram. The levels of radioactive substances found in the soils after applications of the chemical superphosphate are usually <u>double</u> on average and will slowly build up in number as it is applied every season.

You will have to test for nicotine in your soil. When tobacco leaves are preened and their leaves left behind to decompose, it will deposit nicotine in the soil, exposing your soil to mycotoxins because of the decomposition process. Another source of nicotine in the soil is resin the tobacco leaves leave behind during field drying after harvesting. These tests can be hard to find but necessary for areas close to tobacco fields or in water run-off areas of tobacco fields. If you are certain about what was grown on your property, however, you can assume that your ground does contain nicotine. After you grow your mop crops, however, it would be helpful to conduct follow-up tests to gauge the effectiveness of your mop crops.

You will need to test the soil to see if there is any heavy metal concentration from pesticides or herbicides. Chemical pesticides, fungicides, and herbicides contain elements that are not eradicated when people smoke it or through the processing of hemp to make CBD oil, evidenced through the heavy metal chemicals detected in CBD oil. Imagine how long it will take for CBD oil companies to pass the blame onto the growers and join in the lawsuit against you, the grower. If the soil tests positive pesticides, there are certain crops you can plant, such as mint, to draw containments from the ground. Those crops are going to be waste crops that have to be burned away from your growing site. If the pesticides run deep in the ground there's little you can do to get rid of it. Chemical pesticides from long-term use as rainstorms wash the substance further down into the soil.

Mint

You are going to have to test your soil as well for microbials. As we discussed in the previous chapter, microbials are microscopic viruses, fungi, and microscopic spores, and yeasts. Even when microbials burn, they are carcinogenic. They thrive in wet environments and wet soil. Humidity and heavy rainfall are breeding grounds for microbials. If you're soil tests positive for microbials, find a different field. You risk a dangerous, deadly hemp crop. Many buyers of hemp such as dispensaries and processors will not buy hemp without microbial tests from the soil and hemp plants themselves.

You should also test your water system and any natural water source that may be very close to your hemp crop that can run off if it has insecticides or herbicides within it. Herbicides and insecticides can flow over into water sources, including your own. As we recommended earlier, you probably don't want to use natural water sources other than rainwater to water your crop. You wouldn't want to spray that on your hemp as it will absorb the pesticides in that water source. However, if your fields are near a stream that floods your fields every spring from snowy or rainy winter weather, as is the case in our area, you want to regularly test those streams and tributaries to see if they contain any run-off herbicides and pesticides from your neighbors' fields.

One of the things you will need to investigate in your fertilizer or soil is the presence of bugs. Ants will bring in white aphids which will destroy your crop with microbials if they are present. Stinkbugs are a danger to your plants because they will infest your crop as well. Flea beetles from tobacco will also infect hemp and create problems and measures should be taken to get them out of your field, they will be present if a tobacco field is nearby. Tobacco thrips are another species that will climb from tobacco and migrate over to hemp, so it is best to keep an eye out that they aren't in the field already. A lot of hemp damaging bugs can come from corn as well, notably cutworms.

Cut worm damage

It's erroneous to think that you can duck out of testing if you plan on growing your hemp in a greenhouse. If you plan on buying fertilizer, you will need to test the fertilizer regardless of where you eventually wind up applying it. Hemp needs the equivalent of a 30-gallon container to let it grow to full size. This can be a lot of soil to get a hold of and expensive. Soil and fertilizer can sometimes sit around for a while, and you don't always know or can control what environment your fertilizer and soil are stored within. Fertilizer that has sat around for a while or kept in humid conditions can be infected with fungal spores, have grown yeast, or might contain spider mites, ants, aphids. Also, remember that many dispensaries will still require microbial COA's of fertilizer tests for smoking or CBD safety, so growing in containers will not absolve you from these requirements.

If your tests come back with microbials, you will need to go back a step and choose a different field or growing environment. Your field may have had dead infected plant material that had caused a Fusarium outbreak in the soil. We recommend fresh fields that have not had crops grown in it. If you don't have ideal soil or safe soil, a greenhouse is your best option for growing.

Water quality is also a possible source of microbials in cannabis. Heavy metals, bacteria, and other pathogens can exist in your water source being used on your plants against your knowledge. When narrowing down the causes of microbials in cannabis it's best to go to a lab to test your water. If you need to fix your water source, <u>ozonated water systems</u> are used to decontaminate water sources all over the world. They can break down heavy metals and eliminate pathogens. Because ozone breaks down into oxygen, it can give your root systems with higher oxygen levels, which will increase growth. However, <u>the level of ozone you need to kill mycotoxins</u> is not safe for humans. If you use an ozone generator, no human or animals can be near it while it's running.

As explained so far in this book, there are many problems inherited from the soil. More and more companies insist the growers supply microbial and pesticide lab reports in order to show that the plants were not grown in contaminated soil and you have the capacity to grow a safe product. You can test your soil, find out exactly what is in your soil, and grow your industrial hemp crops in pristine conditions. You will also be able to sleep better at night knowing that you have the proof you need in case any problems come down the pipeline.

Now that you have all of the information you need to produce a great, safe product, you will need to carry through great growing and drying practices that will help your plants grow and dry safely. While we will devote an entire book in this series to growing practices, we have some initial advice to offer to get you started.

PART V

GROWING AND HARVESTING

"Mad Hat Hempster" hates total THC

12. GROWING, PRUNING, DRYING, AND IDENTIFYING MALES

As promised, we are going to describe some initial growing, pruning. and drying practices that will help you get started for producing your healthy hemp crop. All of the suggested practices build upon the previous chapters. They will discourage microbial introduction and encourage nice healthy plants.

Planting and Growing

Hemp grows much like corn in that it can grow close together. Tobacco requires about <u>4 feet</u> of width while hemp can be grown close together because hemp grows tall, rather than bushy like marijuana, so it will not interfere with the hemp plants around it as it grows tall. If you begin your plants early enough, it will crowd out the weeds efficiently. It makes it more profitable per acre as well. If you spent the extra money on feminized seeds or clones, this does not mean that you can simply plant your seeds and clones and leave it. Even if you plant in fields, you'll want to check your plants for males every day. You will find a description of what you need to know at the end of the chapter in identifying males.

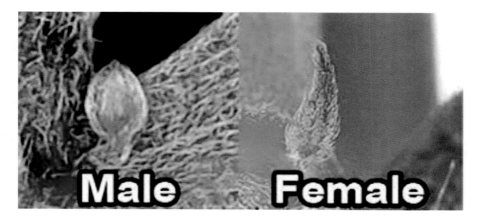

Pruning

Pruning your plants properly will ensure your hemp plants grow straight and tall and produce fine buds. Hemp needs to be trimmed on the bottom, which is similar to tobacco, except with tobacco, you worry about the leaves on the bottom. For hemp plants, you need to cut off the lower branches. Hemp will put all its energy in the lower branches because it's easier for the nutrients to get to without fighting gravity. In fields we have inspected while out on a consulting job, the hemp plant will not grow upward and tall, and the buds and leaves will be small on top while the larger bottom buds will not get enough sun and wilt. Thus, removing the bottom branches on the bottom is an important step in the pruning process.

In addition to removing bottom branches, you want to cut off dead leaves on hemp. Dead leaves take away energy from growth, both taller growth and important leaf growth. They can be identified by their wilt and pale sickly color. They can happen all around the plant and require daily trimming. It should be a part of your daily duties to remove them on hemp.

Removing dead leaves every day will keep the plant healthy

While in tobacco you leave the leaves on the ground, you shouldn't when growing hemp. You are leaving rotting debris around the plant, and it has no natural nutrients to give back to the soil or your growing plants. The leaves on the ground are a host site for bugs to get onto your hemp plant and not only attract them but mice and other nuisance animals that will come and eat those leaves. You will have to pick up the leaves after cutting them off along with the stalks you trim off the bottoms. We suggest you carry around a bag to leave the trimmings in as you cut them off daily. Without this extra work, your plants will suffer. It is not like tobacco. Remember, roses versus eggplants. In this case, what works for tobacco will hurt your hemp crop. In addition, the standards of the two industries are different. You don't want to create beds for bugs that will eat your plants and create dangerous microbials.

In hemp, you need to take care of the plant daily. This becomes laborious if you plan on a large field, and you may need to train helpers to assist you with taking care of your plants. You will need to check for bug-ridden plants, and if confirmed, you will have to rip the plant out and burn it to stop the bugs from spreading further.

Pests, in addition to aphids, can affect the well-being of your plant. You will have to pick off snails. They are not detrimental to a whole crop but they can hurt the individual plants they dwell upon. Snails will eat the leaves and buds and steal nutrients, energy, and growth from the plant. Snails are a harmful if you plan on growing for buds, leaves, or biomass.

Stink bugs can harm your crops. Stink bugs can overrun your crop and chew on the plant which will bring fungi infection. Fungi infections stunt the plant and leave it with low energy. This can essentially kill your crop if left unchecked.

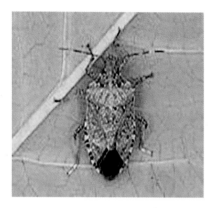

Stink Bug

Biomass companies are timid to buy bug-ridden crops with snails, wasps, aphids, or other penetrating bugs, all of which are happy to make a home in your hemp plants. We have seen all of these when we process plants that were not carefully tended. When crushing up biomass, those bugs could get into the product though their machines, so it would take many hours of handwork to pick them all out and risk some being missed and put into what they are making. It is better to avoid a bad crop in this case, because you don't want to gain a reputation in producing bug oil rather than CBD oil. If the crop is bug-ridden and is unfixable it is better to burn it and start over.

Spider Mites

Helpful Tools

Hygrometers can help you keep track and test your humidity, barometer, and time of day. This can help you see what growing conditions you will be putting your hemp through. We suggest keeping track of what your field or preferably greenhouses humidity and temperature are at different times of day before growing and writing it down. In a greenhouse, it can tell you if you need to add another exhaust fan or if you need to adjust the placement of your atmosphere controlling equipment.

The Farmer's Almanac can help you predict the weather throughout the country through different growing seasons. Let's say you're going to have a warm winter. Then you can start planning to grow early in May if the heat is a suitable temperature for hemp. You can then start dishing your soil in March and disking in gypsum around then. The crop would then be ready about 108 days later, or when the long string-like trichomes on the buds start to turn a rust color. They'd be ready for harvest sometime the end of August to early September. It would be ready to sell after drying for a few weeks after. Farmer's Almanac from our experience is a helpful source for yearly weather reports, and their accuracy is really quite impressive.

Identifying Males

If you are growing flower, high CBD, varieties of hemp you need to plant more than a mile away from another person's crop. If your neighbors grow a male in their crop, it can pollinate up to a mile radius and make your crop go to seed. If your crop of females goes to seed, it will lose 70% of CBD content. This is a major detriment to the profitability of your flower crop. No longer would you have high price seed-free high CBD buds to sell. Instead, you will have low CBD seedy buds that would sell for maybe $2 a bud. This is so much of an issue, <u>Oregon growers</u> have been lobbying their state to make outdoor male cannabis plants illegal. If you are growing outdoors, you will also have to check for wild male hemp plants that could pop up, which could also affect your perfect crop. This matters very little if you are growing for biomass or fiber unless you're growing for seed. If you are growing your crop for seed to sell to other growers, your crop could be pollinated by males of bad genes which could create strains that will easily go hot due to instability in combined genetic lines. Another possibility is producing seed of unknown origin and CBD amount. Say you are growing a perfect crop of 30% CBD hemp that is lower than the 0.3% THC, your neighbors which are 7% CBD pollinates them and instead of getting daughters that would produce 30% CBD, you would get daughter plants that would anywhere in-between 7% or 30% in a 50/50 shot in dark on what the seed will produce, being an unstable first generation hybrid.

With marijuana, many people will buy seeded buds and smoke those as well. In our experience, we have seen hemp buds produce seeds and go hot anyway. However, with hemp, since the concentration is on producing the highest CBD levels possible in the plant, seeds are a major concern. When a hemp plant produces seed, it also lowers overall CBD amount, which can hurt your chances for selling it to CBD producers as well. Most CBD producers are looking for "high CBD" plants. Not much is known on producing high CBD in all hemp plants other than using a flower variety plant and that seeds take CBD production away from the plant, much like a pregnant woman needing more food to grow a child. A plant that should have 12%-13% CBD would come out with 7%-10% CBD if it went to seed. This isn't ideal because anything under 10% is considered low CBD. Even dog food companies won't buy hemp with levels under 10% CBD.

Identifying male industrial hemp plants is not important for all crops, except in the instance you want to keep the ratio of males down and grow mostly females for a higher yield. In fact, having some males is what you strive for when you have grain and seed varieties where the focus is on producing oil and grain. If you are growing grain or fiber varieties, accurately identifying the males is not a major concern. If you are looking to sell and produce seeds to sell this would be the best-case scenario. However, there isn't much you can do with the plant afterward. To extract the seed you will have to tear the plant apart, either with a very expensive and industry-exclusive machine or by hand. The machine will leave very little left of the plant and doing it by hand means tearing apart each sect of the plant and small, underdeveloped buds, looking and investigating each part for seed and picking them out while occasionally crushing up the buds to release them from their pods. From one plant you will receive many pounds of seed and a half a ton to a couple of tons per acre. When you plant the hemp with the same spacing as corn fields, you can fit a thousand plants on each acre. Each plant will produce approximately one to four pounds per plant, but this can vary.

If you intend on growing hemp flower with high CBD, you want to become knowledgeable in identifying male hemp plants. One thing that can ruin an entire hemp crop that is not a concern with tobacco is when hemp plants turn male. When a hemp plant turns male, it can turn every female plant buds within a 3-acre radius into seed. The male hemp pollen impregnates the female flowers, and instead of creating buds, the female hemp plants will create many pounds of seeds instead with small, underdeveloped buds. If you are looking to sell buds, this is very detrimental, and it will make the buds unsellable and make a horrible amount of handwork to pick each seed off. Remember, in certain states, you cannot take the seeds off because that would be manipulating the plant, which you would need a processor license to do. In addition, it can take several months to obtain a new license; thus, your only choice would be to pay a processor to process your seeds for you until your license arrives in the mail or sell your crop for a lot less money than you were hoping.

Many tobacco speakers will tell you the male hemp plants produce the seeds. Yes we've heard people say this, and no, male plants do not produce seeds. We are not talking about seahorses. If you follow that advice you will have a field full of heavily seeded plants. Males do not produce buds, so if you are not producing fiber or seed plants to sell, they are useless and should be either removed, or the male "balls" should be pulled off in case they are a unisex plant. However, you should be aware of the fact that the pollen-filled sacs can grow back as they mature. You read it right. We did this with a male plant, and several weeks later, not only did the pollen sacs grow back, but the plant turned over half of the rest of the plants male in that little experiment.

In addition, there is a chance that plants develop both male (the pollen sacs) and female (pistols) parts—hermaphrodites, making it difficult to tell if there is a male hiding in your plot. Failure to fully investigate your plants for male parts even when they produce female buds can to ruin your whole crop. No such worry exists in tobacco males and females because you are looking for the leaves. In hemp, you are mostly going to look for the males, which can ruin the female plant's flowers by causing the production of seed.

Harvesting

If you are used to harvesting and tobacco, your whole program will have to be changed around for hemp. Most, or even all, of the drying practices of tobacco will be disastrous if applied to hemp. Hemp is a very fragile and disease-prone plant that should be treated in a very different matter.

In harvesting tobacco, you cut it down in the field and leave it in the field for a couple of days before eventually leaving it in a barn to dry out fully. This will not work for hemp. Hemp left out in the field after cutting it down will not have an immune system to resist mold. The mold will affect it immediately as soon as it gets damp. It can mold with the first night's dew, especially during humid times. Bugs will happily take the time to move from the soil to go after the leaves and buds now that they would have easier access. Even if you grew the perfect crop, legal in THC, fully grown, no mold or fungi issues, and severe care of cleanliness, it would be all ruined by leaving it out in the field to dry. Hemp does not dry as easily as tobacco and still would retain moisture.

Any dirt that would get on the buds if you are producing flower would need to get cleaned off or else you would have an unsmokable bud. The problem is, you can't use water to wash it off. It will cause it to mold from moisture if it isn't stored for a long amount of time in a dry place. Extending your drying time to soak the plant leaves it vulnerable to developing mold and fungi. You can't clean it with a cleaner either. It's best just to get your little green jewels into your drying area as soon as you cut them down.

You might want to remember to harvest the roots. You can make a hemp salve from them that is good for arthritis, inflammation, and sore muscles.

Drying

Hemp crops sell for more when they are dried before heading to a dealer or processor. You are going to have to plan or a most importantly dry area to dry your crop. One of hemp's most vulnerable points is during drying. In our consulting experience, growers overlook proper drying techniques most of all. Humid drying conditions will bring on mycotoxins through fungi so you must create a dry space to store your hemp. All the fungi and issues, even with a perfectly grown crop, comes from drying. Improper drying leads to the failure of crops through either infestation of hemp-eating bugs causing dangerous mycotoxins or the penetration of mold and fungi throughout the plant because of humid conditions. One grower we worked with dried it like tobacco as suggested by a tobacco farmer and it had molded out in the field and the buds were filled with beetles making a nest out of it.

Beetle

Leaving hemp out in the field to dry can leave it exposed to conditions it can't handle. Rain can be a major issue as it will add more moisture to the hemp crop. Hemp won't be able to absorb the rain through the roots to use it for nutrition and it would cause the buds to bloat with water. The plant is sure to mold if conditions are too wet, as moisture helps breed bugs and create mold. Ants can swarm field where you drying hemp plants lie and start feeding on the plant which will attract mycotoxin-causing aphids. Ants can be the biggest issue with this as they will seek out the smell of hemp and can crawl anywhere that has an edge for them to crawl on. The secretion on the ants when they eat the plant will bring aphids which bring toxic mycotoxins. Then, you'll be in real trouble.

Bug damage

Hemp plant material can drop off the plant during field drying. The lost buds and profits are the least of your concerns. The dead material would be exposed to mycotoxin-causing bugs and eventually get reabsorbed into the ground causing your soil to get infected for your next crop. Dead material from cutting should be cleaned up between seasons to avoid this regardless of the drying process. If left out in the field, though, you're just asking for trouble. It can create a reliable food source for hemp-eating bugs which may double their count the next growing season as a pest.

If left out in the field, grain and fiber plants can be negatively impacted, as well as your potential profits you will not be able to realize. Grain hemp strains can have their seed yield rotted and mold-covered during the field drying process, which would be a loss in the case of selling seeds for other growers or a loss as selling the seeds for food. Seed yield can get lost in the field and replant themselves in the soil, leading to a late-season, underfed hemp crop that would grow small and die in the winter. This can fill your field with fungi-poisoned hemp from the molded material absorbing into the ground and being reabsorbed by the other crop, which would die and fill your soil back with infected material. Hemp fiber (the stalks) can also rot, making their effective tinsel strength at a loss as well. Nematodes and other stalk-penetrating bugs will go into it and start eating material with ease, bringing bacteria and fungi that will rot the inner fiber. They can essentially eat away at the insides of the fiber which can turn a profitable 8-foot fiber plant into a plant with only 4 feet of profit.

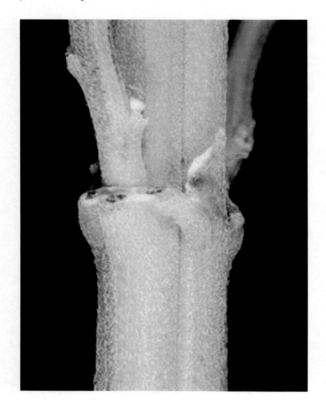

Stalk damage

When drying hemp, a safe space is your best friend. You can use your hygrometer to test a non-humid place for your hemp to dry as the worst toxicity that can happen to your hemp is during improper drying.

In order to create a truly safe drying space, check each of your hemp plant for bugs and to be able to pick them off if they are there before storing the hemp plants to dry. It would be like locking an elementary school in a candy store if you skipped that step. You should also check each plant for mold, mildew, and fungi spots before storing to dry. The dryness of your storage area will help slow spread but combined with buds it can take over your harvested crop.

In your hemp safe place, your drying room, it should be well aired, temperature-controlled area, and low humidity. Dehumidifier's highest setting and fans are going to be of great use. Your temperature shouldn't be below 70 degrees. Controlling your drying environment is as important as controlling your growing atmosphere. This is why an old tobacco barn is not sufficient. We love our old tobacco barn, but since the hot days turn into dew-covered nights, and this includes everything in the barn, including thunderstorms that blanket everything in 100% humidity, we do not use our tobacco barn for drying. Instead, we use it to build custom guitars.

Cleanliness is also going to be important in your drying area and as you work off any microbials and bugs before storing it. As people move in and out, foreign material is tracked throughout a grow room. If this issue isn't fixed it will build up and create contamination from airborne fungi or dangerous bacteria. You need to wear sanitary clothing when handling the plant at vulnerable points in its lifecycle.

There are other factors of post-harvest product handling that can lead to increased growth of microbials in cannabis. Trimming leaves and buds offer the biggest source of human contamination in the entire growing process. Increased yeast levels can be caused by trimmers who aren't wearing the necessary protective gear. Air purification inside of dry rooms can provide excellent defense against outside microbial contamination.

As this chapter advised, even if you do everything right and grow a perfect crop, hemp needs the same level of care in the growing, harvesting, and drying process. If you have acquired certain habits in growing, harvesting, and drying other types of crops, you will be sorely disappointed in your yield in your hemp crops and lose your beautiful plants to fungi, mold, infections, and bugs. Hemp needs to be dried in a controlled atmosphere. For the majority of this book, we have discussed the problems that can come about when treating hemp like tobacco or corn. As explained in this chapter, not even in the drying process can you treat hemp like tobacco. Otherwise, your hemp plants will not survive.

Because hemp is a hotbed for controversy due to its fledgling industry status and certain state and federal laws exist for hemp, in addition with the concern of hemp going hot, this book would not be complete unless we offered some useful advice in contending with the legal aspects of growing hemp. This is not only the aspect that can cause the most confusion because regulations have not been cemented; unfortunately, this is where most of the misconceptions occur for growers, processors, and consumers alike. The fact that hemp regulation is different for each state creates even more confusion and issues. In the last part of this book, we hope to clarify some of these issues, as some of them, if not fully understood, could possibly land you in jail.

Good bugs: ladybugs are a farmer's friend, even for hemp

PART VI

PROTECTING YOUR INVESTMENT: UNDERSTANDING LABS AND FALSE NUMBERS

Bug damage

13. HOT OR NOT: GC VS. HPLC, AND WHY YOUR STATE IS NOT USING THE ONE THAT WILL MEASURE THE TRUE DELTA-9 VALUE

As we write this book, we are approximately two months off from many growers' first hemp harvest. We fear and are predicting that this year will be a firestorm for industry growers because of the legal environment, which might result in a plethora of legal action on both sides, the growers and the state.

While new technologies are evolving all of the time in the hemp industry as it establishes itself over the next decade, there are two main ways to measure the delta-9 THC levels in hemp and marijuana: the gas chromatography (GC) method and high performance liquid chromatography (HPLC). It is important to learn both methods and for you to find out which your state has chosen to measure the delta-9 amount in your hemp. This is the problem with jumping into an industry that does not have established national regulations and protocols. In these beginning phases of the industry, the state and the federal government does not know much about hemp as an industry or substance. There might be times where they people in charge will not make decisions on the best information available. First, let's explain the two methods and why one method is more accurate than the other.

GC and HPLC: Only One Actually Measures the Delta-9 Value

When hemp is tested for its delta-9 levels, the different compounds within the plant are separated, such as CBD, terpenes, and delta-9. The different compounds are then identified through the different speeds they travel. The delta-9 level can be determined through this method.

In the GC method, the hemp is heated until it vaporizes into a gas, and then from there, the delta-9 is isolated. As Rod <u>Kight</u>, advocate lawyer for the hemp industry observed:

> [T]he fact that GC requires heating the sample is particularly problematic for separating Δ9-THC. GC heats the cannabis sample to a temperature that changes its molecular structure in such a way that higher concentrations of the molecule being measured (ie, Δ9-THC) are created. This can cause a sample which initially contains Δ9-THC concentrations within the statutory limit to test above the limit. In other words, the GC technique can, and often does, give a "false positive" result. This transformation is called decarboxylation.

Because the hemp is heated, the process alters the molecular structure of the hemp. Kight likens the decarboxylation process to a radar gun the police use to catch speeders, except the radar has the ability to speed up the car it's measuring. No truly accurate measure can come from that.

In HPLC, the hemp is not heated until it turns into a gas. Rather, it is pressured through a liquid, and all of the substances within the hemp are unaltered. This gives a truer reading of what is actually in the hemp and no corrective formula needs to be employed.

The Corrective Equation for the GC Method Adds to Your Woes: Total THC

Because the GC method does not produce values, but estimations, a corrective equation is employed in order to adjust the values, which further inflates the numbers. It assumes that *all* of the THC, which includes the THC-A, can fully become available, when in fact some of the THC-A never converts into THC depending on how the plant is used as a product. This is why the result of the corrective calculation, the total THC, is an over-inflated number and ***does not measure delta-9 THC***.

We can demonstrate this calculation from a sample lab and apply the corrective formula. Below, we have a lab report that reports the total-THC of the sample.

Report: Evaluation Summary

Product Discription

Client:

Product Name:

Matrix:	Post-Harvest Hemp
Metrc ID:	n/a
Lot Number:	0
License Number:	0
Date Collected:	2018-10-17
Date Received:	2018-10-17
Report Date:	2018-10-24
Tests Requested:	Moisture Analysis
	Cannabinoid Potency Analysis
	Pesticide Analysis

Notes: The sample was collected by the client and PREE laboratory cannot guarantee the sample complies with ORELAP sampling requirements. R&D sample results may not be used for compliance purposes.

Evaluation Summary

Moisture Analysis	Tested Value
	6.25 %

Cannabinoid Potency Analysis |

Compound	Abrv.	Dry Wt. %
Tetrahydro-cannabinolic acid	THCA	0.72 %
Delta9 Tetrahydro-cannabinol	THC	0.11 %
Cannabidiolic acid	CBDA	20.62 %
Cannabidiol	CBD	0.59 %
Cannabinol	CBN	0.00 %
Cannabidivarin	CBDV	0.12 %
	Total THC *	0.73 %
	Total CBD *	18.68 %

Pesticide Analysis	Pesticide Status
	No Pesticides Were Detected above Oregon's action limit as stated in OAR 333-007-0400.

The corrective formula for the GC method is total THC, where they add the value of the THC-A back in and apply a corrective factor to correct for decarboxylation process:

$$THCtotal = (\%THCA) \times 0.877 + (\%THC)$$

When we plug in the numbers from the lab report, we get:

$$THCtotal = (.72) \times 0.877 + (.11) = .73\%$$

As you can see, the results of THCtotal is twice the amount of delta-9 THC value, and this would be considered hot. The state will most like ask this person to burn his crop in an industrial hemp-only state.

Why Your State Might Have Chosen the GC Method

Unfortunately, the GC method is the option that most states chose to use to isolate and test the delta-9 in hemp. It could needlessly land a lot of growers in states that are hemp-legal only in a lot of hot water for no reason at all.

There are a few different possible reasons why your state decided to employ the GC method instead of the more accurate HPLC method. First, they might believe that this is the best test to employ. When we spoke to one of the representatives within our state's agricultural agency that oversees hemp production, that person told us that the Southern states' agricultural departments had a meeting to decide on the best procedures to use for testing. What makes this meeting interesting is their guest: a representative from the Colorado department of agriculture, so they could obtain advise on a matter that they possess no experience and little knowledge.

This is where the problem lies. In Colorado, a marijuana-legal state, they have no concern in distinguishing the difference between marijuana and industrial hemp. They utilize the GC method for their state because the GC method is known for falsely inflating the THC level in their plants. The very act of testing the plants automatically <u>inflates</u> the levels of the substance tested. Growers in marijuana-legal states like this because they can ask more money for their products for high THC levels.

This is the method that the Colorado representative recommended the southern states use. We wouldn't doubt that the fact it is the cheaper of the two tests was a consideration that influenced their decision.

Thus, your state agriculture department could have been misled. If they were, this benefits marijuana-legal states. If all of the possible producers of hemp get into legal trouble for hemp they grew that might not actually be marijuana due to the false positives the GC method produces, this means more burned crops in those states and less competition. The entire nation has no choice but to buy CBD products in marijuana-legal states. While we cannot say for certain if this misinformation was intentional or not, the negative effects on the hemp industry are just the same: barriers to industry entry, loss of investment, and squashing a growing industry.

What You Can Do to Protect Yourself Against Total THC

We recommend that all growers take samples from their plants, possibly at the time the state representative from the same plant and have your own lab that employs the HPLC method instead of GC and fight the results if the state says that your hemp is hot when it is not. We need to tell the USDA that they need to stick to the Farm Bill and require all states to only use the delta 9 configuration and stop using total THC method.

14. A REVIEW AND A LOOK AHEAD

After reading this book, here are some things you should have learned:

- Industrial hemp is a completely different plant in the growing process than tobacco even though it's a smokable product.
- Hemp grown in a tobacco field would have disastrous results with mycotoxins and stunted growth.
- Grain refers to hemp that produces more seeds
- Fiber refers to hemp that grows taller and wider stalks
- Flower is usually used in CBD oil and has high CBD
- Each hemp strain accommodates different industries and you have to be educated what industry matches each strain before growing
- To ensure the survival of the plant, you need to control the environment in where you plan to grow hemp
- Hemp is a temperamental plant that has a lot of predators that can harm a crop
- Hemp stunts in heat above 85 degrees and stresses the plant making it more vulnerable to fungi and bug attacks
- Greenhouse growing is preferable if you are growing smokable hemp so you can control the environment.
- Microbials are a severe health issue with hemp being a consumable and smokable product and must be prevented before it even shows up
- Microbials can be transferred into CBD oil and hemp extracts in this way makes them toxic as well because many microbials survive cooking and boiling
- Hemp is a nutrient sucker and needs a good organic-filled topsoil and rich loam to grow profitably
- Hybrids are marijuana plants crossed with hemp plants and commonly go above the legal limit of THC
- Many clones and seeds are one generation, which makes them unpredictable and weak plants
- It's possible to make a dangerous hemp plant that has endotoxins, mycotoxins, pesticides, and radioactive elements all at the same time like tobacco
- Aphids will bring many issues that will lead to crop loss and toxic plants

- Hemp should not plant in fields that had pesticides, fungicides, and herbicides
- Microbials refer to fungi and bacteria that can harm people
- Mycotoxins are from mold and fungi and are deadly if consumed in large amounts
- Endotoxins are bacteria that can harm people and can be transferred from feces of humans, wild animals, and farm animals to a hemp crop
- Cleanliness and clean farming practices will prevent endotoxins like E.coli and influenza from entering your plants
- Mycotoxins can be prevented through testing the plants you buy, your soil, and your crop at different points of growth
- Molded and fungi-filled hemp plants are a wasted crop
- There is a large learning curve if you have never grown cannabis before

The legislation per state is very complicated and no two states have their same laws for CBD oil, hemp extracts, and cannabis. Our next book shall discuss the up-to-date laws and ramifications of those laws on hemp, marijuana, and CBD oil. It will be a guide for any grower on how their state is letting them grow. It will list which states give full legal access to recreational hemp or marijuana and what states make you have a license to possess it. We will put the laws of each state in simple terms that will be streamlined and easy to understand while providing accurate information. It can give you an understanding of what the legal status is in each state. We will define which states have laws against pesticide use on hemp to help you ensure you are always buying from the safest brands. It will be the definitive travel guide for cannabis and CBD oil and a business guide for selling. Complications abound regarding the understanding of the laws of CBD oil, hemp, and marijuana and who can own it state by state. We will explain which states' laws currently inhibit the hemp industry's growth in that state. We will explain how to get and read a certificate of authenticity for CBD oil or hemp extracts so you know you are always buying a legal product no matter what state you are in. Our guide will help give you a full understanding of all cannabis laws so you aren't a victim of people misinterpreting the laws and holding you accountable for it. You will not have to suffer any longer with misconceptions on hemp regulation again after reading our book. Our goal is to make an informed consumer so you can stay safe and out of legal trouble.

For Your Information:

If you are having an issue with your crop and need answers or need crop consulting, email us at:

hempijuana@gmail.com

We can set up a site visit.

We are also available to do seminars to help explain expert concepts on industrial hemp for Universities, agriculture co-ops, corporate gatherings or events, community centers, expos, etc.
We are open to any organization that wants us to speak at their event, in the USA, Canada, or Europe.

References

Agverra. (2011, April 7). 5 different soil types – Know your soil type. Retrieved from http://agverra.com/blog/soil-types/

Approved Hemp CBD Varieties. (2019, August 7). Retrieved from https://datcp.wi.gov/Documents/IHApprovedCBDVarieties.pdf

Aristotle University of Thessaloniki. (2009). Radioactivity of tobacco leaves and radiation dose induced from smoking. Int J Environ Res Public Health, 6(2), 558–567. doi: 10.3390/ijerph6020558

Aryah, K. (2019, 21 June). North Carolina hemp bill could eliminate smokable hemp-Call to action. Retrieved from https://cannabusiness.law/north-carolina-hemp-bill-could-eliminate-smokable-hemp-call-to-action/

Associated Press. (2019, February 1). Federal crop Insurance available for hemp: Implications for marijuana and the insurance industry. Retrieved from https://www.wglaw.com/News/Newsletters/167608/Federal-Crop-Insurance-Available-for-Hemp-Implications-for-Marijuana-and-the-Insurance-Industry

Associated Press. (2019, July 04). North Carolina proposes ban on smokable hemp. Retrieved from https://nypost.com/2019/07/04/north-carolina-proposes-ban-on-smokable-hemp

Aurum Labs. (2018, December 14). What is "total THC"? Retrieved from https://aurum-labs.com/2018/06/11/what-is-total-thc/

Beaulieu, D. (2019, February 03). NPK is essential fertilizer lingo. Retrieved from https://www.thespruce.com/what-does-npk-mean-for-a-fertilizer-2131094

Bennett, C. (2019, 25 February). How to grow hemp for CBD, seed or fiber. Retrieved from https://www.agprofessional.com/article/how-grow-hemp-cbd-seed-or-fiber

Bennett, J. W., & Klich, M. (2003). Mycotoxins. Clin Microbiol Rev., 16(3), 497–516. doi: 10.1128/CMR.16.3.497-516.2003

Bergman, R. (2019, April 19). Bacterial and fungal controls for marijuana plants (Ultimate guide) - ILGM. Retrieved from https://www.ilovegrowingmarijuana.com/bacterial-and-fungal-controls/

Bergman, R. (2019, May 07). Stop Fusarium on marijuana plants now! Retrieved from https://www.ilovegrowingmarijuana.com/marijuana-diseases-fusarium/

Berke, J. (2018, March 27). Mitch McConnell wants to legalize hemp - Here's how it's different from marijuana. Retrieved from https://www.businessinsider.com/what-is-hemp-different-from-weed-2018-3

Bienenstock, D. (2019, April 04). Is legal hemp about to ruin America's outdoor cannabis crops? Retrieved from https://www.leafly.com/news/industry/legal-hemp-pollen-drift

Bjarnadottir, A. (2018, September 11). 6 Evidence-Based health benefits of hemp seeds. Retrieved from https://www.healthline.com/nutrition/6-health-benefits-of-hemp-seeds#section1

B. U., Nwaka & N. N., Jibiri. (2018). External and internal radiation doses from chemical fertilizers used in Ibadan, Oyo State, Nigeria. Retrieved from https://globaljournals.org/GJSFR_Volume18/8-External-and-Internal.pdf

Charles, S., M.D. (2019, April 24). Popular e-cigarette products contaminated with bacterial and fungal toxins, study finds. Retrieved from https://www.nbcnews.com/health/kids-health/popular-e-cigarette-products-contaminated-bacterial-fungal-toxins-study-finds-n997781

CBD Oiled. (n.d.). History of hemp - From 10,000 BC. Retrieved from https://cbdoiled.com/history-of-hemp-from-10000-bc/

Centennial Seeds(2015, July 30). Limited release high-CBD BaOx seeds. Retrieved from http://www.centennialseeds.com/page/3/

Centers for Disease Control and Prevention. (n.d.). Health effects of cigarettes smoking. Retrieved from https://www.cdc.gov/tobacco/data_statistics/fact_sheets/health_effects/effects_cig_smoking/index.htm

Conley, S. P., Gaska, J., Roth, A., Skjolees, C., Silva, E., Ortiz-Ribbing, L., . . . Robinson, P. (n.d.). Industrial hemp agronomics. Retrieved from https://fyi.extension.wisc.edu/hemp/industrial-hemp-agronomics/

Corrigan, R. (2018, November 28). Which soil is best for planting tomatoes? Retrieved from https://homeguides.sfgate.com/soil-planting-tomatoes-25144.html

Cothren, J., & Gryder, J. (2014, October 8). Johnsongrass in pastures can be toxic. Retrieved August 15, 2019, from https://wilkes.ces.ncsu.edu/2014/10/johnsongrass-in-pastures-can-be-toxic/

Cornel CALS. (n.d.). Fertilizers for corn. Retrieved from https://fieldcrops.cals.cornell.edu/corn/fertilizers-corn/

Cox, J. (2018, December 08). Methods to stop Botrytis on cannabis (Bud rot, gray mold). Retrieved from https://moldresistantstrains.com/stop-botrytis-on-cannabis-bud-rot-gray-mold/

Crouse, D. (n.d.). Soils and plant nutrients. Retrieved from https://content.ces.ncsu.edu/extension-gardener-handbook/1-soils-and-plant-nutrients#section_heading_7241

Dauke, M. Korner, M. Katzlberger, C. (n.d) Monitoring of radioactivity in fertilizers in Austria. Retrieved from http://www.irpa.net/members/P10.14.pdf

Davis, J., & Kendall, P. (n.d.). Preventing E. coli from garden to plate. Retrieved from https://extension.colostate.edu/topic-areas/nutrition-food-safety-health/preventing-e-coli-from-garden-to-plate-9-369/

DEA Museum. (2019, August 12). Cannabis history. Retrieved from
   https://www.deamuseum.org/ccp/cannabis/history.html

Decorte, T. (2011, September). Fibre hemp and marihuana: Assessing the differences
   between distinct varieties. Retrieved from
   https://www.votehemp.com/PDF/Fibre_hemp_and_marihuana-
   Working_Paper_Series_no_38.pdf

Dich, J., Zahm, S. H., Hanberg, A., & Adami, H. O. (1997). Pesticides and cancer.
   Cancer Causes Control, 8(3), 420-43.

Drug Abuse Editorial Staff. (2019, June 11). Is marijuana addictive - Physically and or
   psychologically? Retrieved from https://drugabuse.com/marijuana-
   addiction

Ellsworth, J. (2019, January 07). Microbials in marijuana. Retrieved from
   https://willowindustries.com/microbials-in-marijuana/

Ellsworth, J. (2019, June 24). Eliminating microbials in marijuana. Retrieved from
   https://willowindustries.com/eliminating-microbials-in-marijuana/

Flax. (2019, August 14). Britannica, T. E. Retrieved from
   https://www.britannica.com/plant/flax

Franciosi, A. (2018, October 04). Trichomes: The complete guide. Retrieved from
   https://honestmarijuana.com/trichomes/

Geaseeds. (2018, March 20). Types of fungi in cannabis – Prevention, remedies and
   treatments. Retrieved from https://geaseeds.com/blog/en/types-of-fungi-
   in-cannabis-prevention-remedies-and-treatments/

Gill, L. L. (n.d.). Can you take CBD and pass a drug test? Retrieved from
   https://www.consumerreports.org/cbd/can-you-take-cbd-and-pass-a-drug-
   test/

Globalhemp. (2013, October 23). Hemp for victory. Retrieved from
   http://www.globalhemp.com/1942/01/hemp-for-victory.html

Gontar, R., & Nielsen, L. (2019, February 01). Botrytis cinerea: Controlling this
   devastating plant disease. Retrieved from
   https://www.epicgardening.com/botrytis-cinerea/

Goodhemp (2019, July 05). Hemp Oil Vs Olive Oil: Blog. Retrieved from
   https://www.goodhemp.com/hemp-hub/why-you-should-swap-olive-oil-
   for-hemp-oil

Greenfacts. (n.d.). A global evaluation of the impact of mycotoxins contaminants on
   food safety. Retrieved from https://www.greenfacts.org/en/mycotoxins-
   aflatoxins-fumonisins/l-2/index.htm

Hemp. (2019, August 06). Britannica, T. E. (Retrieved from
   https://www.britannica.com/plant/hemp

Hemp Basics. (n.d.). Hemp uses, information facts. Retrieved from
   https://www.hempbasics.com/shop/general-hemp-information

Hemp Industries Association. (n.d.). Hemp history. Retrieved from https://www.thehia.org/history

Hemp Industries Association. (n.d.). Hemp textiles. Retrieved from https://www.thehia.org/Textiles

Hemp Industry Daily. (2018, April 11). Hemp state highlight: Tennessee fights humidity, lack of processing in bid to gain market share. Retrieved from https://hempindustrydaily.com/hemp-state-highlight-tennessee-fights-humidity-lack-processing-bid-gain-market-share/

Hemp Tech Global. (n.d.). Basics. Retrieved from https://hemptechglobal.com/page83/page83.html

Hodgson, E. (2012). Progress in microbiology and translational science. Available from https://www.sciencedirect.com/topics/agricultural-and-biological-sciences/cannabaceae https://doi.org/10.1016/B978-0-12-415813-9.00014-3

Hossain, Farazi, MH, A., & MAA, M. (2018). Effects of consecutive two years tobacco cultivation on soil fertility status at Bheramara Upazilla in Kushtia District. J. of Rice Res, 6(1), 190.

IARC Working Group on the Evaluation of Carcinogenic Risk to Humans. (1970, January 01). AFLATOXINS. Retrieved from https://www.ncbi.nlm.nih.gov/books/NBK304413/ Bookshelf ID: NBK304413

Jaeger, K. (2019, July 03). USDA Head is worried farmers will grow too much hemp. Retrieved from https://www.marijuanamoment.net/usda-head-is-worried-farmers-will-grow-too-much-hemp/

Jenkens, H., E.(n.d.). Studies on the Tobacco Crop of Connecticut. Available from https://books.google.com/books?id=6-ZFAQAAMAAJ&pg=PA30&lpg=PA30&dq=Phosphate makes tobacco leaves grow bigger&source=bl&ots=A6FSkc60RQ&sig=ACfU3U2WJQr64QZagSCChh8fNkns53Z-Sg&hl=en&sa=X&ved=2ahUKEwjtnsmzofnjAhWPW80KHaj2DX0Q6AEwEHoECAkQAQ#v=onepage&q&f=false

Kaplan, S. (2018, November 10). F.D.A. Plans to seek a ban on menthol cigarettes. Retrieved from https://www.nytimes.com/2018/11/09/health/fda-menthol-cigarettes-ban.html

Keeler, J. (2019, June 18). Can you overdose on marijuana? Retrieved from https://www.wikileaf.com/thestash/marijuana-overdose

Kight, R. (2018, December 3). Hemp testing 101: Analytical testing protocols explained and evaluated. Kight on Cannabis. Retrieved from https://cannabusiness.law/hemp-testing-101-analytical-testing-protocols-explained-and-evaluated/

Kossen, J. (2019, July 11). How cannabidiol (CBD) works for treating anxiety. Retrieved from https://www.leafly.com/news/health/cbd-for-treating-anxiety

LaLiberte, K. (2019). Organic garden soil: Use organic compost more. Retrieved from https://www.gardeners.com/how-to/building-healthy-soil/5060.html

Lamota. (2015, November 24). Powdery mildew and downy mildew: How to deal with two of marijuana's biggest threats. Retrieved from https://www.lamota.org/en/blog/powdery-mildew-and-downy-mildew-marijuanas-threats/

Leafly. (n.d.). ACDC Cannabis strain information. Retrieved from https://www.leafly.com/hybrid/acdc

Leafly. (n.d.). T1 Trump hemp flower. Retrieved from https://www.leafly.com/products/details/ihf-llc-t1-trump-hemp-flower

Lecours, N., Almeida, G. E., Abdallah, J. M., & Novotny, T. E. (2012, March 01). Environmental health impacts of tobacco farming: A review of the literature. BMJ Journals, 21(2). http://dx.doi.org/10.1136/tobaccocontrol-2011-050318

Leonard, P. (n.d.). pH for the garden. Retrieved from http://pss.uvm.edu/ppp/pubs/oh34.htm

Martin, T. (2019, May 16). How cigarettes contain dangerous radioactive chemicals. Retrieved from https://www.verywellmind.com/radioactive-chemicals-in-cigarettes-4121185

McCarthy, N. (n. d.). Which states made the most tax revenue from marijuana in 2018? Forbes. Retrieved from https://www.forbes.com/sites/niallmccarthy/2019/03/26/which-states-made-the-most-tax-revenue-from-marijuana-in-2018-infographic/#77d0395d7085

Mckeil, J. (2019, April 24). The evolution of merchant services for the hemp industry. Retrieved from https://www.cannabistech.com/articles/the-evolution-merchant-services-for-the-hemp-industry/

McKernan, K. (2017, October 03). Botrytis cinerea. Retrieved from https://www.medicinalgenomics.com/botrytis-cinerea/

McLaughlin, R. (2019, April 15). Can plants grow in Sand? Retrieved from https://dengarden.com/landscaping/Can-Plants-Grow-in-Sand

Medical Genomics. (2019, May 24). Aspergillus: The most dangerous cannabis pathogen. Retrieved from https://www.medicinalgenomics.com/aspergillus-dangerous-cannabis-pathogen/

Melamede, R. (2005). Cannabis and tobacco smoke are not equally carcinogenic. Harm Reduct J., 2(21). doi: 10.1186/1477-7517-2-21

Miksen, C. (2018, December 14). How to correct high phosphorus levels in soil. Retrieved from https://homeguides.sfgate.com/correct-high-phosphorus-levels-soil-28597.html

Ministry of Hemp. (n.d.). What is hemp?: Learn about the hemp plant. Retrieved from https://ministryofhemp.com/hemp/

Ministry of Hemp. (n.d.). Hemp vs marijuana: The difference between hemp and marijuana. Retrieved from https://ministryofhemp.com/hemp/not-marijuana

MMJDoctoronline. (2016, June 18). Why smoking moldy weed is bad, bad news. Retrieved from https://mmjdoctoronline.com/health-news/why-smoking-moldy-weed-is-bad-bad-news

Moldpedia. (n.d.). Mycotoxins. Retrieved from https://moldpedia.com/mycotoxins

Muggli, M. E., Ebbert, J. O., Robertson, C., & Hurt, R. D. (2008). Waking a sleeping giant: The tobacco industry's response to the polonium-210 issue. Am J Public Health, 98(9), 1643–1650. doi: 10.2105/AJPH.2007.130963

National Cancer Institute (2019). Cannabis and cannabinoids (PDQ®)–Health professional version. Retrieved from https://www.cancer.gov/about-cancer/treatment/cam/hp/cannabis-pdq

National Institute on Drug Abuse. (n.d.). What are marijuana effects? Retrieved from https://www.drugabuse.gov/publications/research-reports/marijuana/what-are-marijuana-effects

NCCIH. (2018, October 25). Marijuana and cannabinoids. Retrieved from https://nccih.nih.gov/health/marijuana

Newhopseed. (n.d.). Starting and growing tobacco from seeds. Retrieved from https://www.newhopeseed.com/tobacco_growing.html

Newman, S. Pottorff, L.P. (2019 May) Powdery mildew. Retrieved from https://extension.colostate.edu/topic-areas/yard-garden/powdery-mildews-2-902/

NORML - Working to Reform Marijuana Laws. (2019, May 23). Report: Majority of commercially available CBD products contaminated with heavy metals. Retrieved from https://norml.org/news/2019/05/23/report-majority-of-commercially-available-cbd-products-contaminated-with-heavy-metals?link_id=21&can_id=f0781f99b54624da943bbae4f6bb3d86&source=email-norml-news-of-the-week-5232019-2&email_referrer=email_553140&email_subject=norml-news-of-the-week-5232019

North Carolina Agriculture Department. (2019, 21 March). North Carolina farm act of 2019. Retrieved from https://www.ncleg.gov/Sessions/2019/Bills/Senate/PDF/S315v1.pdf

Nuclear Safety Commission. (2014, February 03). Polonium-210. Retrieved from https://nuclearsafety.gc.ca/eng/resources/fact-sheets/polonium-210.cfm

Nunn, S. (2019, June 9). The south's economy is falling behind: 'All of the sudden the money stops flowing.' Wall Street Journal. Retrieved from https://www.wsj.com/articles/the-souths-economy-is-falling-behind-all-of-a-sudden-the-money-stops-flowing-11560101610

Oil Seed Crops. (n.d.). Hemp. Retrieved from http://www.oilseedcrops.org/hemp/

Oregon State University. (2017, March 31). Mycotoxins. Retrieved from https://pnwhandbooks.org/plantdisease/pathogen-articles/common/fungi/mycotoxins

Ortiz, J. L. (2019, February 05). No smoking? Hawaii lawmaker wants to say goodbye to cigarettes forever. Retrieved from https://www.usatoday.com/story/news/nation/2019/02/05/smoking-ban-hawaii-aims-ban-cigarettes-tobacco-legislation/2774631002/

Pauly, J. L., & Paszkiewicz, G. (2011). Cigarette smoke, bacteria, mold, microbial toxins, and chronic lung inflammation. J Oncol. doi: 10.1155/2011/819129

Pennsylvania Nutrient Management Program. (n.d.). Managing phosphorus for crop production. Retrieved from https://extension.psu.edu/programs/nutrient-management/educational/soil-fertility/managing-phosphorus-for-crop-production

Penn State University. (2018, 02 July). Industrial hemp production. Retrieved from https://extension.psu.edu/industrial-hemp-production

Pests.org. (2018, March 28). How to get rid of groundhogs: Updated for 2019. Retrieved from https://www.pests.org/get-rid-of-groundhogs/

Pests.org. (2019, August 15). How to get Rid of moles: Updated for 2019. Retrieved from https://www.pests.org/get-rid-of-moles/

Place, G. (2019, 02 May). Hemp production – Keeping THC levels low. Retrieved from https://catawba.ces.ncsu.edu/2018/11/hemp-production-keeping-thc-levels-low/

Plant Village. (n.d.). Tobacco. Retrieved from https://plantvillage.psu.edu/topics/tobacco/infos

Probst, C., Njapau, H., & Cotty, P. J. (2007, April). Outbreak of an acute aflatoxicosis in Kenya in 2004: Identification of the causal agent. Retrieved from https://www.ncbi.nlm.nih.gov/pmc/articles/PMC1855601/ doi: 10.1128/AEM.02370-06

ProCon.org. (1999). What is THC (Delta-9-Tetrahydrocannabinol)? Retrieved from https://medicalmarijuana.procon.org/view.answers.php?questionID=000637

Pruet, J. J. (2019, February 15). Report: lab tests of CBD oil reveals 'startling results,' including pesticides and lead. Retrieved from https://www.theblaze.com/news/cbd-oil-tests-pesticides-lead

Purdue University Hemp Project. (n.d.). Hemp production. Retrieved from https://dev.purduehemp.org/hemp-production/

Rahn, B. (2019, May 17). Indica vs. sativa: What's the difference between cannabis types? Retrieved from https://www.leafly.com/news/cannabis-101/sativa-indica-and-hybrid-differences-between-cannabis-types

Richter, C. (2019, April 29). Growing tobacco in the home garden. Retrieved from https://www.richters.com/show.cgi?page=InfoSheets/d6492.html

Rideout, J. W., & Gooden, D. T. (2000). Effects of starter fertilizer. Retrieved from https://www.tobaccoscienceonline.org/doi/full/10.3381/0082-4623-44.1.19

Rogers, S. (2011, March 15). Radiation exposure: A quick guide to what each level means. Retrieved from https://www.theguardian.com/news/datablog/2011/mar/15/radiation-exposure-levels-guide

Royal Queen Seeds. (2017, August 23). How to protect your weed plants from a fungal Fusarium invasion. Retrieved from https://www.royalqueenseeds.com/blog-how-to-protect-your-weed-plants-from-a-fungal-fusarium-invasion-n609

Schell, J. (2019, January 12). Michigan marijuana failed E. coli, salmonella and chemical tests. Retrieved from https://www.foodpoisonjournal.com/food-recall/michigan-marijuana-failed-e-coli-salmonella-and-chemical-tests/

Seedfinder. (n.d.). BaOx (Centennial seeds): Cannabis strain info. Retrieved from https://en.seedfinder.eu/strain-info/BaOx/Centennial_Seeds/

Selmar, D., Engelhardt, U. H., Hänsel, S., Thräne, C., Nowak, M., & Kleinwächter, M. (2015). Nicotine uptake by peppermint plants as a possible source of nicotine in plant-derived products. Agronomy for Sustainable Development, 35(3), 1185–1190.

Shahul Hameed, P. Sankaren Pillai, G. Mathiyarasu, R. (2014). A study on the impact of phosphate fertilizers on the radioactivity profile of cultivated soils in Srirangam (Tamil Nadu, India). Journal of Radiation Research and Applied Sciences, 7(4), 463-471. https://doi.org/10.1016/j.jrras.2014.08.011

Springer Science+Business Media. (2015, April 8). Plants can take up nicotine from contaminated soils and from smoke. ScienceDaily. Retrieved August 19, 2019 from www.sciencedaily.com/releases/2015/04/150408090342.htm

Society for General Microbiology. (2014, April 15). Pathogenic E. coli binds to fresh vegetables. ScienceDaily. Retrieved August 18, 2019 from www.sciencedaily.com/releases/2014/04/140415203813.htm

Texas A&M AgriLife Extension. (n.d.). Field guide to common Texas insects. Retrieved from https://texasinsects.tamu.edu/greenbug-aphid/

The Chill Bud. (2016, January 14). Hempcrete - The revolutionary 'Green' building material made from cannabis. Retrieved from https://thechillbud.com/hempcrete-the-revolutionary-green-building-material-made-from-cannabis

The Household Cyclopedia of General Information. (1881). How to Grow Tobacco. Available from http://www.publicbookshelf.com/public_html/The_Household_Cyclopedia_of_General_Information/howtogro_ee.html

Todar, K., & Madison. (n.d.). Bacterial endotoxin. Retrieved from http://textbookofbacteriology.net/endotoxin.html

Tweedlefarms. (n.d.). AC/DC - Outdoor. Retrieved from https://tweedlefarms.com/products/acdc?variant=7991918002229

United States Department of Agriculture-Farm Service Agency. (n.d.). The current threat to U.S. tobacco farmers and their communities. Retrieved from http://govinfo.library.unt.edu/tobacco/PRFiles/I-Current%20Threats%207-10.pdf

University of Kentucky. (n. d.). Aphids. Retrieved from https://entomology.ca.uky.edu/ef103.

USDA. (n.d.). Industrial hemp. Retrieved from https://nifa.usda.gov/industrial-hemp

Virginia Department of Agriculture and Consumer Service (2018). Annual report on the status and progress of industrial hemp research program. Retrieved from https://rga.lis.virginia.gov/Published/2018/RD563/PDF

Virginia Department of Agriculture and Consumer Services, Office of Pesticide Services (2019). Pesticide use on hemp. Retrieved from http://www.vdacs.virginia.gov/pdf/pesticide-use-on-hemp.pdf

Wagers, K. (n.d.). Is white powdery mold harmful to humans? Retrieved from https://www.hunker.com/13427877/is-white-powdery-mold-harmful-to-humans

Weixel, N. (2019, July 06). Lawmakers grow impatient for FDA cannabis rules. Retrieved from https://thehill.com/policy/healthcare/451652-lawmakers-grow-impatient-for-fda-cannabis-rules

Welsh, P. (n.d.). Never add clay to sand or sand to clay. Retrieved from https://www.patwelsh.com/soils/never-add-clay-to-sand-or-sand-to-clay/

World Health Orignization. (n.d.). Tobacco: The smoke blows south the environmental costs of tobacco production. Retrieved from

https://www.who.int/tobacco/framework/public_hearings/panos_institute.pdf

World Health Organization. (2018, May 9). Mycotoxins. Retrieved from https://www.who.int/news-room/fact-sheets/detail/mycotoxins

Young, E. (2008). Radioactive polonium in cigarette smoke. Retrieved from https://scienceblog.cancerresearchuk.org/2008/08/29/radioactive-polonium-in-cigarette-smoke/

Zagà, V., & Gattavecchia, E. (2008). Polonium: The radioactive killer from tobacco smoke. Pneumologia, 57(4), 249-54.

Made in the USA
Columbia, SC
04 February 2021